Praise for A

"As one of the head writers for my TV show *Maron,* Michael was essential in helping me portray myself honestly. I'm very happy and impressed that he was able to apply his craft to himself. It's not easy to put your authentic "you" out there. Michael did a beautiful job of it with *A Paper Orchestra."*

— Marc Maron

"Fantastic.... It's multi-timbral. It runs all levels of the pyramid at the same time. His knockout punches are stinging sincerity."

— John Mayer

"My eyes are still misty. Michael was a writer on a show I did, and I know he's funny. That's his gift and his profession. I did laugh out loud, that I expected. But what I appreciated most was being led into his thoughts, down the path to his deepest confessions and deepest loves. Good storytelling also leads us to ourselves, our memories, our beliefs. Personal and powerful. I loved the journey."

— Laura San Giacomo

"Those who appreciate the power of simple stories to tell us about human nature... or who are bewitched by a storyteller who has mastered his craft, will find a delightful collection of vignettes.... A lovely anthology that strikes a perfect balance between humor and poignancy."

— *Kirkus Reviews*

"Keen, hilarious, and sometimes heartbreaking insights from an astute and twisted observer of everyday life."

— Steven Levitan, co-creator, *Modern Family;*
creator, *Just Shoot Me*

"While I was laughing out loud, my heart was breaking.... Tragedy and comedy in one."

— Judy Greer

"As the father of daughters, I found Michael's understanding of parenting and the human condition to be spot-on. This book is a fantastic read!"

— Max Mutchnick, co-creator, *Will & Grace*

"Brisk, engaging storytelling and dialogue.... *A Paper Orchestra* offers as many heart-tugging moments as laughs."

— *Booklife Reviews*

"I had some much-needed laughs and was touched by so many of Michael's observations about love and life."

— Ty Burrell

"*A Paper Orchestra* is a joy. It is funny, but with depth and resonance that is a revelation.... I loved this book."

— John Altschuler, co-creator, *Silicon Valley*

"A hilarious and heartfelt collection of stories. I give it my highest praise — I wish I had written it."

— Jonathan Aibel, writer, *Kung Fu Panda*

"Michael Jamin was always one of the fastest guys in the writers' room with the perfect joke. Now, reading his book, *A Paper Orchestra,* I realize he can also write honest and powerful stories that stick with you long after reading them. So, in true Hollywood fashion, I must now root against him."

— Dave Krinsky, showrunner, *King of the Hill*

"I found myself laughing and loving the wit which Michael Jamin tells his stories with, only to be blindsided by his incredibly emotional, poignant confessions that hit me at the core."

— Steve Lemme, *Super Troopers, Beerfest, Tacoma FD*

"It's at times funny and at others sad, and sometimes manages to catch you off guard by being both at the same time. It's a thought-provoking, witty, and engaging look at human nature and the way we often treat each other."

— David Litt, co-creator, *The King of Queens*

"With *A Paper Orchestr*a, Michael effortlessly achieves the big three as a writer. He's smart, heartfelt, and very funny."

— Kevin Heffernan, *Super Troopers, Beerfest, Tacoma FD*

A Paper Orchestra

Michael Jamin

3 Girls Jumping

First published in the United States in 2024 by 3 Girls Jumping.

Author's note: The events described in these stories are real, although the chronology may have been compressed. Other than for those closest to me, the names and details of the characters have been changed to protect their privacy ... even if they don't deserve it. But of course they do. But do they really?

Cover design by Jenny Carrow.

Cover art by Toon Joosen.

ISBN 9798988650409 (pb) 9798988650430 (hc) 9798988650416 (eb) 9798988650423 (ab)

Library of Congress: 2023912203

3 Girls Jumping 101 North Verdugo Road #9874 Glendale, CA 91206

michaeljamin.com

For Cynthia, Roxy, and Lola Mia

What if the smallest, almost forgotten moments were the ones that shaped us most?

Contents

A Paper Orchestra

Escape from Kelly Jelly Belly

I had a bad feeling about dating Kelly. I know why I did it, though. It wasn't out of loneliness, but that certainly played a part. I just didn't know what else I should do with my free time. High school and college made it easy. There were papers and exams to prepare for. Reading and supplemental reading. If you never wanted to think for yourself, school was heaven. But I had recently graduated, and now I was in the real world, where everyone made their own schedule. This was hard for me. When I wasn't working, I was free to do whatever I wanted. "But shouldn't I be doing something else?" I constantly wondered, even while I was doing something I enjoyed.

That's how I wound up taking an architectural-drawing class at UCLA Extension. For only $200 I could block off a few hours and just be compliant. It was there that I met Kelly, who sat behind me. We made eye contact on our first day of class, when I passed her the sign-in sheet. Her long brown hair was pulled up, and she chewed gum loudly, in a way that suggested she didn't really care. I found that to be reassuring.

Other than that first interaction, we never spoke. None of the students spoke to each other. It wasn't that kind of class, although the 40-year-old woman I shared a table with told me she worked at *Playboy.* She said it with a wink, hoping that I'd find her exotic and maybe even slutty. For a moment my interest was piqued, then she said she was an accountant and the spell was broken.

The class met at an outdoor mall called the 3rd Street Promenade. I hated that word: "promenade." It sounded like a cross between "prom" and "odd," and that's kind of what it was to me —a weird place to spend an awkward occasion. The mall really came alive at night, which only added to my unease. Was this the right location for a night school? It didn't feel scholarly enough. Yes, I could be here, but should I be here? Existential angst is what a therapist told me I had—that dreaded sensation of never feeling you're in the right place. Even as she diagnosed me, I was thinking, "Should I be talking to someone else?"

For class, I always parked in a garage a few blocks away, in the same spot on the fourth floor. That way, I wouldn't have to fret about finding my car afterward. It was always right where it was supposed to be—and that was one less decision I had to make. As I was pulling into my usual spot, I noticed Kelly getting out of her red Mitsubishi, right next to me. I parked without thinking and immediately regretted it. Why couldn't I roll the dice a little and just park a few spots down? Now Kelly and I would have to walk to class together and things would be weird. I suppose I could've followed a few feet behind her, but at some point she'd inevitably turn around, recognize me, and wonder why I was stalking her. I decided that my only choice was to break the ice and just be super-casual about the whole thing.

"Hey, what's going on, dude?" I said, as if talking to an old friend carrying a surfboard.

A puzzled look came to her face, and my stomach dropped when I realized that Kelly had absolutely no idea who I was. In retrospect, we had that in common. I didn't know who I was, either. But I was going through an identity crisis. What was her excuse? Four times in class I had turned around to hand her that sign-in sheet. Four times! Was I that unmemorable? It was one of those embarrassing moments that causes permanent damage to your DNA, the trauma of which gets passed down to later generations. A hundred years from now, my great-great-grandson would wonder why he had an inexplicable fear of talking to people in parking garages. He could thank Kelly for that.

"I sit in front of you in class," I reminded her. Still no glimmer of recognition from Kelly, so I continued. "At UCLA Extension." And then to be 100 percent clear, I added: "Where we are both heading right now."

"Oh, right. Hi!" responded Kelly, and my heart finally started beating again.

"Oh, right. Hi" was literally the least she could offer me. It would've been nice if she had made a joke about it, blaming herself for her shoddy memory, but instead I was left to feel desperate and needy. We headed to the stairwell, where we walked 48 steps before reaching the ground floor. I counted. But something magical must've transpired during that time, because when we reached the ground floor, Kelly was a completely different person. Whatever discomfort she displayed in the garage had been replaced with bubbly enthusiasm—like her whole body had been carbonated in the stairwell. She became effusive, leaning into me to share how she saw the world.

"Look at that wank," she said conspiratorially while touching my shoulder. "With his white leather shoes. I bet he's dripping in cologne." She was referring to a middle-aged man coming out of a restaurant with his younger girlfriend. She wore high heels, which made him look even shorter.

"Look how she's standing. She hates him," said Kelly.

They were standing apart, but how did Kelly know she hated him? That's not to say that Kelly was wrong, but how was she so certain? I admired this. She didn't seem to be struggling with the world the way I was.

"We should hang sometime," she said as we walked into the classroom. She said it loud enough for the *Playboy* accountant to hear, who in turn, coyly raised her eyebrows at me, as if she'd just been invited into a threesome.

It sounded like Kelly was asking me on a date. I didn't really think Kelly was my type, but after the way things ended with my ex-girlfriend, I wasn't even sure if I had a type anymore.

"Call me *here,*" said Kelly, writing her number on a piece of paper. There was something strange about the way she accented the word "here"—as if she had the potential to be in two places at the same time. I couldn't even be in one place at the same time.

"Sure. I'll call you *here,*" I responded.

* * *

Finding Kelly's house was another riddle. According to the address on the curb, she lived in a swanky, two-story Spanish Colonial in Beverly Hills with arched windows and a stuccoed courtyard lined with pink-and-yellow bougainvillea. I thought Kelly was too young to be a self-made millionaire, but I guess she could be a trust-fund baby. Or maybe she was kept, like the woman at the Promenade who hated her boyfriend. Something about this felt very off. I compared the address on the house to the one that Kelly gave me: 129 1/2. I had never heard of a half-address before. Did she live in the floor joists between the first story and the second story?

I ventured down the driveway, annoyed that Kelly hadn't given me clearer instructions. Why make me feel like a trespasser?

It's not like I was serving her a subpoena. The driveway was lined with birds-of-paradise and other tropical plants, and it felt like, at any moment, a Rottweiler would lunge out of the bushes, sending me scrambling over the neighbor's fence, where another Rottweiler would lunge at me, ping-ponging me back over. Dammit, Kelly.

The driveway led to the guesthouse, where string lights draped over the patio. It looked like a fancy bistro—the kind of place where you glance at the prices on the menu, then decide you're in the mood for soup. It didn't seem right that Kelly lived on this property, given her age. I thought everyone was supposed to live the way I did—in a small one-bedroom with bars on the windows.

I paused at the front door to compose myself, but before I could even knock, the door flew open. It was Kelly, and she quickly pulled me inside.

"I'm so happy you made it! Did you find it alright? Was the traffic bad? Did you do the homework yet?" Her rapid-fire left no room for me to answer, and it was disorienting. It reminded me of a nature show I once watched, where a grizzly bear was standing in a river trying in vain to catch one of the hundreds of salmon flying past his head. Too much. Just too much!

"Come. You want a tour? I'll give you a tour?" Now she was grabbing my hand, leading me through her home. With her other hand, Kelly popped jelly beans into her mouth by the fistful. She'd pluck them out of glass jars that were posted about like highway signs: LAST SUGAR FOR SIX FEET. A jar of purple jelly beans was stationed next to a purple candle, a jar of orange jelly beans was next to an orange vase, and there was a jar of black-and-white jelly beans on top of a TV set.

"Is that a black-and-white TV?" I asked.

"Black-and-white? No, it's color. Why would it be black-and-white? I wouldn't have a black-and-white." That's how I discovered that Kelly's bubbly demeanor wasn't natural—she was jacked on sugar. We continued following the trail of jelly beans, which surprisingly led to her bedroom and not a unicorn's nest. Within moments, I was sitting on Kelly's bed, questioning her decision to fill an ant farm with green jelly beans. Shouldn't they be white? No, don't ask! And in case it sounds like I'm being overly dramatic, the pillow on her comforter said: KELLY JELLY BELLY.

Kelly threw a few more jelly beans into her mouth as she crossed to her stereo, where a CD was playing. She tapped the fast-forward button a few times, trying to find the right track.

"Nope, not that one ... Not that one ... Not that one."

"Do you ever, like, eat vegetables?" I asked, making a brief excursion to planet Earth.

Kelly plunged her hand deep into a fishbowl and pulled out two jelly beans—one red; the other, light green.

"Tomato and cucumber!" she laughed.

"Tomato is actually a fruit," I replied, but perhaps I wasn't making my point.

By now, I had a pretty good idea that Kelly and I weren't headed to the altar, unless it was one where she performed human sacrifices. "Has she been saying Kelly or Killy?" I wondered.

Then she threw herself next to me on the bed, and began playing with the curls of my hair. "Whoa, this is going fast," I thought.

"Close your eyes and open your mouth," she said.

Uh-oh. She was going to jam her tongue down my throat, wasn't she? I shut my eyes, and was relieved to hear the rattling of a nearby jar of jelly beans. But also disappointed. What can I say about that, other than I'm a guy.

"Aren't you worried all this sugar kinda messes with you?"

"That's a myth," she replied, as she placed two jelly beans

onto my tongue. "What does it taste like to you?" Before I could even guess, she shouted, "One's marshmallow and the other's chocolate. It's Rocky Road, dummy!"

Now she was banging on a conga drum, and I closed my eyes even tighter. How is Kelly still alive? Her heart must be pounding like a hummingbird, and I wondered if I'd catch her drinking sugar water from a bird feeder.

"So do you have reservations?" she asked.

You fucking better believe I have reservations, I wanted to say. I didn't, though. Instead, I just muttered, "Yep, I'll feel better when I'm surrounded by witnesses."

The car ride to the restaurant was interminable, with Kelly babbling about jelly beans, which, to be fair, was at my prodding. I'm certain she mistook my morbid fascination with her diet to be genuine romantic interest.

"What about Red Hots? Do you like Red Hots?"

"On Valentine's Day I do," she replied. I smiled weakly.

"So you're a writer," she said, finally changing the subject. "Maybe you'll write about me someday."

"Oh, I'll definitely write about you someday." And she blushed. So did my knuckles, which were gripping the steering wheel for dear life.

I was hoping Kelly might settle down at dinner, once she got some actual food into her candy-coated bloodstream, but the breadsticks only made her eccentricity grow stronger. She was now pitching me the film she dreamed of making. That's not a figure of speech. She literally had a dream, and now she was looking for backers to film it. Soon, the waiter came over and asked if everything was okay.

No, I considered blinking in Morse code. But he was referring to the meal, and not my welfare. The waiter left, and Kelly launched into the shot list of her film.

"We open on our hero, seven-year-old Kelly ... that's me ... walking down the boardwalk. "One Lover at a Time," by Atlantic Starr, plays in the background. Do you know that song?"

"No."

"I'll sing it for you."

Five months later, when I was finally driving her back home, Kelly began cozying up to me. She was convinced we were now boyfriend and girlfriend. I, on the other hand, was already in the breakup phase of our relationship, wondering how many rum-raisin jelly beans she'd drown her sorrows in.

I was so disappointed. A few days ago, I thought Kelly had it all figured out. I wanted to be in her grace just to have some of that confidence rub off on me—so that I wouldn't feel so much at sea. I must've been preoccupied by this thought, because Kelly gently ran her fingers on my arm and said, lovingly, "Are you okay, sugar?"

Of all the possible moments that could have been my breaking point, it's ironic that this was the one that pushed me over the edge: a hypoglycemic calling me "sugar." And of course, I handled it wrong. I could've responded to Kelly with kindness. I could've been delicate and thoughtful. But instead I went with the old standby: sarcastic asshole. From experience I knew that "sarcastic asshole" never pays off, but in this case, I guess I was willing to give it another try.

"When you say 'sugar,' are you talking to me or your toxicology report?"

And with that, Kelly Jelly Belly's personality soured like a gobstopper. Apparently, all the subtle jabs I made throughout the evening weren't lost on her. I took her to be a vacant fool, but if anyone was absent, it was me. And that last jab, the one that I assumed would go over her head, was the straw that broke the caramel's back. And yes, I do mean "caramel." It was her second-favorite flavor.

Kelly launched into a breakup speech that, to a bystander, would've suggested she had given me the best 10 years of her life, instead of the most surreal two and a half hours of mine. The windows to my car were down, and I'm certain that as we idled at the intersection, people in neighboring cars heard her unloading on me, wondering what heinous act I had committed. Despite her fury, I managed to say nothing during the remainder of the ride, muttering only to cast magic spells to make the traffic lights turn green. When I finally pulled up to her home, she stormed out of the car, slammed the door, then stomped around to my window, where she glared at me.

"Are you coming in or not?"

* * *

"I can't believe you didn't go in!" laughed my friend Alex.

"And wind up chained to a radiator, chewing through my arm?! No, thanks."

We were hanging out at a coffee shop one evening after work. Alex was one of the first friends I made when I moved to L.A. I met him at a barbecue that my roommate invited me to. He was funny and down to earth, and I appreciated him for being so welcoming. Even though he was only in his mid-20s, Alex was already married, which added to my own insecurity. Not that I wanted to be married, because I didn't. It just felt very grown-up of him.

Despite enjoying his company, my eyes kept glancing at the large blackboard over the counter, where the menu was written in colored chalk. It was beautifully done, with ornate lettering. It made me think that the person who wrote it, clearly an artist, was in the wrong place, too.

"I have just the girl for you," said Alex. "I'm gonna set you up with Leanne."

This was a new wrinkle in Alex's story, as he had recently gotten divorced. Despite years of pretending that he wasn't, Alex had finally come to terms with the fact that he was gay. Selfishly, I was glad to hear that. It was reassuring to know that I wasn't the only one who didn't know who he was. Back when he was straight, Alex never once tried to set me up. But now that he was gay, he was a matchmaker.

"I know," he laughed. "I'm really diving headfirst into this gay thing."

As he described Leanne to me, I watched the people reading the menu on the blackboard, and I wondered if they shared the same level of concern that I had for the artist who wrote it. There were all types of people at that counter. Hipsters, posers, crunchies ... but it was the goth chick that really caught my eye. She was dressed head to toe in heavy black clothing. With her thick, dark lipstick and eye shadow, her outfit screamed "Look at me" and "Don't look at me" at the same time. "Figure out what you want," I said under my breath. "Then help me do the same."

"Leanne is a little overly focused on med school, but I keep telling her to relax," said Alex. "So don't take it personally if she comes off cold. Do you want to meet her?"

"Not even a little."

"Well, you should. She's hot. Unless you're gay now, too."

I wasn't gay, so I agreed to go on a blind date with Leanne. We met at a breakfast café, and she sat down opposite me, never quite getting comfortable. Instead, she perched at the edge of her seat at an angle with her torso facing the door, ready to bolt. When our server came, she ordered a smoothie to go. The message she sent to me was undeniable. It couldn't have been clearer had she studied the menu and finally said to the waiter, "You know, I think I'll have the Time Bomb. And if you can set it to five minutes and leave it under his seat, that would be great."

Surprisingly, Leanne didn't actually take her smoothy to go. Instead, she drank it at our table, then spent a full hour telling me how busy her life was. She had exams and labs and more labs, and because of that, she was too busy for a relationship.

"Relationship? What the fuck are you talking about, honey?" I yelled. Actually, I only yelled it with my eyes. Aloud, I said, "Do they make you take classes on bedside manner?"

"Last semester. It was a waste of time." Yes, apparently it was.

As she lectured me about the incredible hardships of almost being a doctor, my mind took a leap into the future. What would Leanne's life look like in 20 years? She'd definitely have a successful career in medicine, but what would her personal life look like? She wouldn't live in an expensive house. That would require too much maintenance. A doctor who couldn't even keep a lawn alive—what kind of message does that send? No, she'd live in a condo on the Westside. Her balcony would have a great view, but she'd only enjoy it on Memorial Day, when she forced herself to host a brunch for her co-workers. Her second husband would be nothing like the schlub she married the first time. That guy was far too needy, requesting sex four times a year. Husband No. 2 would be older than her, and have a hectic life of his own, traveling the country on business and ordering top-shelf whiskey at airport hotels. He claimed to love the excitement of life on the road, but only I knew the truth.

He should just leave Leanne. So should I. We should both get up and leave Leanne. If there was one bright spot from this horrible date, it was that despite her outward show of confidence, Leanne was just as lost as I was.

"Ooh, look at the time," said Leanne, checking her watch. "I'm sorry I have to run, but it was such a pleasure meeting you."

"You didn't meet me," I thought. "You just talked about yourself. I met *you.*"

Then Leanne informed me that her busy schedule wouldn't permit us to go on a second date.

"Oh. So *that's* the reason why there wouldn't be a second date?" I shot back with my eyes.

* * *

Cynthia was a guest star on the sitcom I was writing for. Her character was supposed to be a potential love interest for one of the regulars. So that's the first time I laid eyes on her—on a soundstage, pretending to be on a bad first date, which was something I knew a lot about.

It was a small part, just one scene, but all the writers were excited to watch it because the character we created was so unusual. She had an innocence, and Cynthia was able to capture it. With her soft, raspy voice and dark-brown eyes, she was lovely. She performed the scene with such warmth, connecting with the lines so that we didn't just hear them, we felt them. Screenwriters love actors who can do that well. Not just because they're great on-camera, but because they make our own words surprise us.

We shot the show on Friday night, and after every taping, it was custom for the cast and crew to gather at a nearby restaurant to celebrate the small victory of putting a show on its feet, as well as the giant victory of being employed in Hollywood. Our group took over a private room, and it was common at these events for everyone to mingle ... especially with the agents that magically appeared, even though they weren't invited. They circled the party like vampires, and we happily served up our bare necks to them. One bite, and they could offer us immortality, which, in Hollywood parlance, meant another three to five years of work.

I ran into Cynthia at the bar and complimented her performance. It was honest and funny, and you could tell the audience absolutely loved her. When I mentioned this, she smiled. The approval meant a lot to her, and I saw it not just in her face but deep in her eyes. It made me think of peering into a well and spotting something shiny at the bottom. A wish.

We found a quiet corner to talk, away from everyone else. There was something about the way she spoke, or maybe it was the way she listened, that made me not want to share her. She seemed to be so grounded. At some point, I got so comfortable that I almost steered the conversation over a cliff by making a reference to an ex-girlfriend. She broke up with me in a way that was so cavalier and reckless, it made me doubt she ever loved me at all. It was such a vulnerable thing to say, but I said it anyway, the way you'd confide in a stranger, safely knowing that you'd never see them again.

"That's not for you to say," Cynthia corrected me. "That's her journey. It's just as hard for her as anyone else." She stated it with such certainty, and it caught me by surprise. I guess I was hoping she would take my side. Blind allegiance. But instead she reacted with empathy for someone she had never met. That was a quality that I rarely saw in people, including myself, and it seemed so generous. To me, empathy felt like energy going out. It was giving instead of getting, and I didn't think I could afford to give anything away.

"How can I be like her?" I thought.

A week later, I was picking Cynthia up for dinner. She lived in a dicey part of Hollywood, although to be fair, the drug dealers didn't seem to mind. But that's not why I was hesitant as I climbed the stairs to her apartment. I was afraid that an intimate look at her home would disappoint me. A sad addiction to corn syrup, maybe.

"What's going to be wrong with this one?" I thought, looking up the flight. It was a difficult staircase, in that there was no landing at the halfway point. No place to pause and catch your breath. Just one unbroken climb, all the way up, and it seemed like a long trip to take every day, just to be at home.

Finally at the top, I knocked on her door, and when she opened it, her eyes lit up. It reminded me of how I felt the other night at the bar. Not just looked at, but *seen.*

"Come on in," she said, and she disappeared into her bedroom to find a coat.

My eyes quickly scanned her living room, looking for clues or maybe warning signs. We both lived in comparable one-bedroom apartments. Dingy and run-down. But hers was so strikingly different. Mine was filled with the cheapest furniture Ikea had to offer—the same soul-less pieces that everyone bought, so I just did the same. Cynthia's home, on the other hand, was sparse but handpicked. Almost curated. I walked to her shelf, hoping to judge her by the books she kept, but she only had a few. And on her refrigerator, where so many people slap old photos of friends and family, there were none.

"Where's her past?" I wondered, as the rustling of coat hangers carried into the kitchen.

I couldn't have possibly known this at the time, but Cynthia was hiding her past. It was a secret that I would learn much later, when things between us got serious. She shared it only with the people she loved, and we hadn't declared that to each other yet. The night we ate dinner on her patio, she almost told me. It was just a small ledge with a depressing view of an alley, but with the fairy lights she strung around the potted plants, the space looked enchanted. I had just said something that I thought was funny, and turned to her, expecting a laugh. But she seemed distant, lost inside herself. I could tell she was about to say something, but then, just as quickly, she backed away, like it was a door to something horrible and dangerous. Something that might devour you whole. Instead she hid among the fairy lights, which cast the faintest glow on her.

"You'll tell me when you're ready," I said quietly.

That moment came a few weeks later, when I heard her crying in my bedroom. I ran in, thinking she had injured herself, and I found her curled in a ball on my futon.

"I want to tell you," she sobbed. "I'm just scared that you'll look at me differently." This time I didn't allow her to disappear. This time I insisted, taking her hand so that maybe some of her fear would leave her body and flow into mine.

I sat in silence as she told me her story. I learned how she grew up poor, the only child of a single mother. She was an unwanted pregnancy who grew into an unwanted child. I learned that her mother struggled with alcoholism and would often send her to the grocery store with the welfare check to buy a jug of wine. And I learned about the man who lived in her building. He wanted her when no one else did. He gave her attention, took her places, bought her things, and all of that made her feel good. But the abuse didn't. She was only seven years old. And it lasted five years. She told me about the court trial she attended, when he was finally caught, and how she and her best friend waited to testify, along with all the other girls whose childhoods he had taken away. And she told me how he eventually died in prison, by his own hand.

The years of suffering had left its mark. For almost her entire life, it made her feel ugly, and ashamed, and unworthy of feeling any kind of joy. But now, after having spent so much time at the very bottom, she was determined to save the rest of her life. And she had a plan to do it.

"Just please," she cried, "don't look at me differently."

But of course, I didn't yet know any of this as I stood in her apartment for the first time, trying to size up her life. How could I?

What I saw was a tattered blue couch that had been rescued from the flea market. With a few throw pillows resting against the arms, the couch almost looked grateful for the second chance. In the corner stood an antique lamp with a scarf over its torn shade to hide its scars. There was an old dining room table with four mismatched chairs that deserved some love, too. On the stove was a chipped red pot, and a pan with a wobbly handle. This was a life that Cynthia had reclaimed. She pieced it together little by little, hanging on to things that brought her joy and letting go of things that didn't. It was a collection, and it was meant to serve as an anchor, keeping her right here in the present. I lingered, somehow sensing the profoundness of it, wondering how she had figured it all out.

"Ready," she said, and I turned to see her standing just beyond the darkness of the hallway. How absolutely beautiful she was. As we headed out the door, I gave one final look at all the imperfect little things she had saved.

Maybe she could save me too.

Yellow Belt

"Send down the queen!"

As a child, that's how I summoned my mother when I was snuggly in bed and ready to be tucked in. It was the conclusion of my evening routine that began with me gathering my stuffed animals and stationing them around my bed, like a pharaoh going to the underworld. I liked that because it's a title that's even higher than "king" or "queen." A man-god. My parents were brought to me, and not the other way around.

After calling off, my mother would arrive at my bedroom door, and I'd gesture for her to kiss my forehead but act annoyed about it—like it was an honor for her and a nuisance for me. When she was done fawning, I'd announce, "That is all. Send down the king," and my father would do the same.

"Tell me a story," I demanded, as he entered. I really enjoyed his stories, so I don't know why I added condescendingly "and make it a good one this time."

Most of his stories were about his days in basic training. It was never his goal to be in the army, but this was during the Vietnam War, and he had no choice. That's how Private First Class Jamin came to be. Leave it to the federal government to think they could turn a Jewish nerd from the Bronx into a killing machine.

In basic training, my father was regularly dehumanized by his insane, anti-Semitic drill sergeant. "I want a hundred push-ups, Jamin, or you'll be scrubbing the latrine with your Jew toothbrush!"

My father hated being in the army. Every minute of it. But the stories he told about his time as a recruit always ended with him laughing hysterically. Somehow, with the distance of time, the degradation became charming and nostalgic. And that's how my father sent me off to dreamland—not with images of candy canes and rainbows but with the sadistic taunts of a Jew-hater.

Back then, my bedtime was at a strict eight P.M. During the winter, when the days were short, that seemed reasonable. But during the summer months, it was still light outside. How was I expected to fall asleep when I could hear the neighbor kids laughing and riding their bikes?

"Lights out, pal," my father would say, and he'd flick the switch, leaving my bedroom as bright as it was before.

"But my feet can't breathe!" I'd often shout.

That was another common refrain from me. My blankets had to be just right—not tucked in but not completely untucked, either. My feet had to be able to poke out of the bottom, just enough for them to breathe, like they were snorkels. I'd make such a fuss out of it that my mother had no choice but to return and re-adjust my blankets. My father hated this. He thought it was coddling, and it made him second-guess the way he was raising me.

"Don't be such a Fauntleroy!" he'd say.

I didn't know who Little Lord Fauntleroy was, but in context, I could tell it wasn't a compliment. I had a lot of weird habits back then. Constantly licking my fingers was another one. It was something I needed to do if I was touching certain fabrics, like corduroy. There was something about that texture that made me wince to handle it, and dipping my fingers in my mouth made it slightly more bearable, even if it made me look like a moron. Picture a professional bowler wiggling his fingers above a fan. That's what I looked like, only the fan was my tongue.

I was delicate that way. While other boys my age enjoyed playing contact sports, I shied from it. All the pushing and shoving, and for what—to kick a ball into a net? How about we just leave the ball where it is and melt crayons into candles that smell weird.

Those were the activities I enjoyed. Peaceful ones, like constructing miniature houses for imaginary creatures. I built one beneath the dogwood tree in our front yard. It was made out of twigs and leaves, and had a layered ceiling to keep out the rain. Every morning before school, I'd walk outside and check on it. I'd lay my head against the ground, the dirt rubbing against my cheek, and look for sunshine poking its way through the roof. Those were the areas that needed shoring up, so that the raindrops couldn't make their way through. With a well-placed pebble or twig, all the imaginary creatures could find shelter, and feel cozy and safe.

"I think we should sign you up for karate lessons," said my father one day. "It'll toughen you up. Like boot camp." My eyes went wide in horror. Karate was the last thing in the world I wanted to do. Contact sports were bad enough, but karate didn't even have the pretense of moving a ball down the field. There was only one objective, and that was to inflict bodily harm on your opponent. My father's proclamation felt like a prison sentence, and I nervously plunged my thumb into my mouth, sucking on it like it was filled with heroin. My other hand raced to the side of my head, where I rubbed the cuticle of my thumb against the hard ridge of my ear. That was another one of my weird idiosyncrasies, and it made me look like a field reporter about to deliver a big scoop.

I'm certain my father only wanted what was best for me. He must've felt obligated to prepare me for a hostile world—one where kids would sense my weakness and bully me because of it. He didn't want that. He wanted me to stand tall and be proud of who I was. Ironically, to make that possible, I'd have to become someone I wasn't. I've been on both sides of this problem: first, as a child; then later, as an adult with my own children. Do I encourage them to go down the path they're best suited for, or push them to step out of their comfort zone? It's hard to know which is more loving.

I spent that week worrying over the fate that might befall me in karate class. Maybe someone would smash my head into a pile of bricks. Or maybe they'd launch a roundhouse kick into my face, sending me into a wood chipper. But as the days passed, I heard nothing more about karate class, and assumed my parents had forgotten about it. It wasn't long before I returned to my old, carefree self, sliding down rainbows into lakes of chocolate syrup.

I was watching *Gilligan's Island,* eating my afternoon snack, wiping my sticky fingers on the carpeting, when my blissful tranquility came to an end.

"Mommy, do we have any more cinnamon-raisin bread?" I shouted. "The kind glazed in white frosting." It was really more of a cake, but my mother called it bread, so it would sound like good parenting.

"No time," she hurriedly replied. "I'm taking you to judo."

Judo? Panic set in. The organized beatdown hadn't been canceled. It had only been delayed and rebranded. My first instinct was to weasel out of it on a technicality.

"But Dad said *karate!*"

"Judo's got 'Jew' in it. Good enough."

* * *

I sobbed in the car on the way there. The idea of organized violence terrified me. But crying like a baby was the wrong way to handle it. It suggested that judo lessons were exactly what I needed.

The class was held in the basement of a local strip mall, beneath a nail salon, so their entrances were right next to each other. I "accidentally" reached for the wrong door, and feigned surprise at the sight of three women with their feet dipped in large tubs. I looked at my mother expectantly, as if to say "Shall we?" but she pulled me in the other direction, away from the fumes of nail-polish remover and toward something even more toxic. As we descended the staircase to the martial arts studio, my hands brushed against the cinder block walls. They were cold and damp, as if they, too, had just finished a good cry.

The studio itself was little more than a floor covered with a white canvas mat. Its brightness was stark and unwelcoming. Old black-and-white photos of Japanese men hung on the wall, next to a flag of the rising sun. They must've been martial artists, and their expressions ranged from solemn to weary. Beneath the nail salon, the Battle of Okinawa was still raging.

"*Osu,*" said the instructor as he bowed to me, and I looked to my mother for a translation. She just shrugged.

"Remove your shoes and put this on," he said, while handing me an oversize white robe called a "*gi.*" It was as bad a fit for me as judo itself, with its stiff and scratchy collar spilling off my narrow shoulders like an egg yolk dripping out of its shell.

"I don't understand," I complained to the instructor. "How am I supposed to put the belt on? There are no loops."

"The belt doesn't hold up the pants," he responded gruffly. "It holds the robe shut."

"Oh, so it's more of a sash."

It's hard to imagine sending a clearer signal that I had no business being in a martial arts studio. Did I have to ride in on a unicorn? Yet the instructor didn't want to hear it. In me, he saw not a future warrior nor a scared little boy, but $50 worth of lessons. Raphael was his real name, and he was a middle-aged Latino man who walked with a limp. He claimed it was the result of an injury he suffered while sparring, which is the wrong thing to say to a child already on the verge of blacking out.

In Raphael's right hand was a long bamboo pole that he carried like a prop. To be honest, I appreciated the theatricality of it. He held it the way one might hold an umbrella on a sunny day —lightly and with a flourish whenever emphasis was necessary. My opinion of this pole quickly soured when I realized its true purpose. He used it to smack us.

"Form!" he'd shout.

"Yes, *sensei!*" Then he'd beat someone across the back with a sickening crack.

No one bothered telling me what *sensei* meant, but in context I interpreted it to mean "asshole." "Yes, asshole!"

The pole was split lengthwise into four parts that were woven together so that its sections clapped, thereby producing more noise than pain. I didn't know this, of course, so the first time he cracked a student with it, I almost vomited. I did everything perfectly that day.

"So tell me what you've learned so far?" asked my father excitedly when I returned home. "Can you smash a brick with your head?"

"I can count to 10 in Japanese." I quickly demonstrated, and I could see his face fall in disappointment.

"The first two are easy: *ichi, ni*. It sounds like 'itchy knee,' and that's easy to remember because these pants are scratchy."

"Itchy knee," he repeated while shaking his head in disbelief. The man sent to me to judo class so I could fight like Luke Skywalker, and instead I came home talking like C3PO.

For several months, I suffered through these classes, and eventually *sensei* announced I was ready for my yellow-belt test. That was part of the racket. I wasn't good enough to reach the next level, but it meant my parents would have to shell out money for another 10 classes, plus a new belt. Truthfully, I was only proficient at falling to the mat—that, and counting to 10 in Japanese, which impressed Keiko, a girl at school who introduced me to a Japanese art form that was more my speed: folding origami. Fortunately, the paper was smooth, but not soft, so I was able to touch it without mopping my fingers down like a cat.

On the day of the test, *sensei* called out each move, and I fudged my way through them while he guided my limbs with his bamboo pole like I was his marionette. At times I giggled, because I was ticklish, just like all the great judo warriors who came before me. Of the various moves I was required to remember, maybe three or four of them I got right, yet *sensei* awarded me the yellow belt just the same. Given enough time, I'd be swinging a black belt around my neck like a feather boa, and he could finally pay for that hip surgery he needed.

Afterward, *sensei* announced we were all going to fight in a local competition, and the class erupted in cheers. But not me. I was stunned silent. Despite the fact that martial arts were meant for fighting, I assumed it would never come to that. "I'm warning you. I know judo!" was supposed to be an empty threat—just something you yelled before your enemy ran away in fear.

I looked around to see if any of my classmates shared my apprehension. Not the two green belts standing next to me. They were already slamming each other against the mat in excitement, their baggy pants barely hiding their erections. I closed my eyes—willing myself to be somewhere else.

In the ensuing weeks, instead of training for the competition, like everyone else, I just held still. I was a terrified rabbit hiding in plain sight, afraid that even a twitch might draw attention to myself. At home, I didn't practice my moves or hone my technique. I simply told myself lies: that whatever I knew would be enough, and that whoever I was would be plenty.

The fight was held at a local rec center, and it was my father's idea to get us there early. That way, he could find a folding chair to sit on, and I could scope out the competition. That was also his idea. Secretly, I hoped I'd face off against someone like me—someone more interested in braiding key-chain lanyards than yelling "*Ki-yah*" with blood dripping out of his eyes. The crowd hummed with anticipation, the excitement of which fed the contestants, who were psyching themselves up. I found a quiet little hole to hide in along the walls of the gymnasium. Above me, someone had graffitied the Grateful Dead logo. It was a blue-and-red skull with a lightning bolt going through it, and it made me feel uneasy. It wasn't so much the image that frightened me but the knowledge that a vandal had been in this same exact spot, and might return at any moment. Someone who was grateful for being dead.

I spotted my *sensei* sitting with the other *senseis* at a large folding table that functioned as a registration desk. He was wearing his street clothes—jeans and a T-shirt underneath an old flannel shirt. It was odd seeing him out in public. In my mind, he existed only on the white canvas mat of our judo studio, having been imprisoned there by an evil warlock, who would turn him into a puddle of water if he ever tried to escape. I waved at him, hoping he'd offer me comfort or encouragement. He could be a mentor or an ally—either would be fine. Instead, he gave me only the slightest glimmer of recognition, just a small nod, and I knew I was alone.

Once the matches began, I watched aghast as the other kids attacked each other violently. I became paralyzed with fear, staring at the savagery before me. My father, who was seated next to me, must've seen it in my eyes, because he touched my arm to get my attention, and I flinched.

"Be aggressive," he said.

"Aggressive" was a word he had recently taught me because it was an attribute that I rarely showed. I didn't like aggressive people. They struck me as obnoxious bullies, and now I was supposed to be like that? I didn't have the faintest idea how to be aggressive. It just wasn't in me.

My name was called over an old loudspeaker, and it came out muffled and dry, which is exactly how it would've come out of my own throat.

"Michael Jamin," it announced. I stepped gingerly to the center of the mat. I took my time, to give fate a chance to intervene on my behalf. Maybe there'd be an earthquake or a tsunami, or some other welcome calamity that would cancel the tournament. I had no such luck, though.

Center ring, my gaze met the referee's, hoping that he would recognize the fear in my eyes and call the whole thing off. Adults were supposed to have that power, right? They're supposed to protect kids in trouble. They're supposed to give voice when children can't find the words. Not this adult, though. He glanced at his watch, then signaled for my opponent to approach. He was a kid my age, maybe younger, lost in his own head as he shadowboxed the match that hadn't yet started. He was fighting before there was even reason to. His moves were quick and varied, and if it was meant to intimidate me, it worked. He looked like he was trying to escape from a straitjacket. He may have had real-world experience in that, because when he raised his face, I saw a crazed look in his eyes. It penetrated the mop of wavy red hair dangling from his forehead like a bloody shower curtain hiding a murder scene. His nostrils were pointy triangles, and he looked feral, as if his parents had grown weary of telling him to stop eating the paint chips off the wall and just finally released him into the wild, where he would catch squirrels using only his mouth. I didn't catch his name, but Kyle would've been a good guess.

I looked around at the audience circling the mat. Everyone was watching me, which felt odd. If this were a play, I could have given them a dance or a laugh. If it were a concert, a tune. But this was a judo competition, and I had nothing to offer them. Or so I thought.

The ref had us bow to each other. That felt calm and respectful, and for a moment, I thought there might be hope—like we had settled our differences and could now leave in peace. But then the ref motioned for us to begin, and in an instant, everything changed. Kyle was released from the imaginary iron shackle around his neck. Pouncing off the floor, he leaped at me, opening a Costco-size jar of pickled crazy along the way. His arms were swinging like one of those ornamental ducks people keep on their lawns—the kind whose wings spin furiously in the wind and make you think, "What the fuck is wrong with that duck?"

The crowd exploded into cheers, as if they had paid to see a gladiator fight. Kyle grabbed my arm, but summoning all my coward courage, I yanked it free. Forget about countering—I didn't want to engage him. My only goal was to keep far away from Kyle's windmill limbs of death. I moved backward, farther and farther from him, looking for an escape route. Sensing my fear, he lunged at my waist and slammed me ferociously against the mat. I would've screamed in pain, but the air coughed out of my lungs before I could do so. Now he was roping my arms like a steer at a rodeo, flipping me into submission. I flailed on the mat while he smothered me from above, twisting my limbs in directions they weren't meant to move, and I huffed, fighting for my life. Because he was shorter, the crowd assumed that Kyle was the underdog, and with each attack, they grew more excited, gorging themselves on the blood sport of it all.

I cowered in a ball, covering my face with my arms, hoping someone would come to protect me. With the crowd egging him on, Kyle proceeded to beat all that was weird, weak, and different out of me. "Get him! Get him!" shouted someone nearby, and others quickly joined in. Even with his knee against my ear, the roar was deafening, and I wondered what I had done to cause everyone to hate me so much.

By now my *gi* had been ripped down to my waist, splashing me with cold air. I wanted to pull it back on, but Kyle's arm was wrapped around my neck, and I could feel his savage breath against my face while I gasped for air just to stay conscious. My head was pressed flat against the mat, the grit from dirty feet rubbing against my cheek. From this angle, I saw only one thing clearly: my yellow belt lying unfurled in the middle of the floor. My free hand strained toward it, but I don't know if I was trying to pull it closer or push it farther away. It must have been this gesture that the ref finally saw, because in an act of mercy, he called the fight. The crowd erupted, and Kyle's arms launched toward the heavens in victory as I lay crumpled on the mat, half naked.

When I found my breath, I slowly took to my feet and pulled my *gi* back over me, covering my humiliation. But it wasn't my body that the audience reacted to. It must've been the terrified look on my face, because everyone fell silent. It was no longer fun for them, and they felt dirty for having enjoyed it. I never wanted any of this. None of it. That must've been obvious.

My father and I sat in silence during the ride home. I felt small sitting in the front of his car, and with each bump in the road, I sank further into the seat, hoping to eventually disappear.

"You did great out there," he finally said. "Really great."

He said it with a softness in his voice while not quite looking at me, so that I couldn't see the lie. I turned my head toward the window, trying to hide my face as I wondered how soon it would be before I had to get the shit kicked out of me again.

"We've had enough judo for a while, don't you think?" he suggested.

Maybe in that moment, my father realized that he had been mistaken, that all his fond memories of being dehumanized in the army weren't meant to build character. They were meant to destroy it, turn men into something they weren't so that they would follow orders instead of their hearts.

I didn't know what I was supposed to say or who I was supposed to be, so instead my eyes moved to my feet, as if the correct response were written next to the Volkswagen logo on the floor mat. I nodded and wiped my tears with my sleeve.

When we pulled into our driveway, I got out of the car, then slowly crossed the lawn, returning to the house of twigs, beneath the dogwood tree. It had been months since I last worked on it, and the roof was crumbling. Half in ruins, it looked sad and forgotten. I sat down on the grass and gathered a few sticks in my lap. On the horizon, rain clouds were rolling in, and the small creatures would need to feel safe again.

Masks

When I was young, there was a popular children's cartoon about a special little boy. He didn't have a rare talent, or an advanced intellect, but he was dead, and that did make him stand out. Despite being a ghost, which would undoubtedly cause most people to bemoan the cruelty of their untimely demise, this young lad was surprisingly chipper. In fact, he only wanted to focus on one thing: spreading good cheer. Heartbreaking, really. The show was called *Casper the Friendly Ghost,* and the creators were quick to add the qualifier "friendly" so that overly sensitive children like myself wouldn't shit themselves out of fear. It was reassuring to know that this ghost didn't want to drag me to the underworld, unlike the ghost lurking inside the steamer trunk my parents kept in the basement.

As a television writer, it's hard for me to imagine how this show got sold. If I tried to pitch it, I'm certain TV executives would put me through the wringer.

"So, this dead kid. What hilarious way did he die? Leukemia? Sudden-infant-death syndrome?"

"My plan is to never address that."

"Uh-huh. And his parents ... they're inconsolable, right? Absolutely devastated?"

"I have a happy spin on that. They died when he was a baby."

"Yeah ... That's a pass."

Yet somehow, *Casper the Friendly Ghost* was green-lit and became a mainstay of pop culture. Growing up, I watched every episode, having decided it was just the right level of terrifying for me, which is to say, as scary as a glass of milk. As a child, I wasn't just afraid—I was also afraid of being afraid. I'd bend over backward so that I wouldn't have to do something even remotely scary. I was almost heroic that way. My best friend, Adam, didn't seem to be scared of anything. He bragged about watching *The Exorcist* and *Jaws.* Not me, though. I couldn't even watch *The Incredible Hulk*—and he was a good guy! I guess he was too green for me. But watching *Casper* allowed me to feign a certain level of machismo. I could tell Adam that I, too, enjoyed watching ghost stories while leaving out the embarrassingly lame details. If someone had asked me back then what I was like, I might've described myself as a "pussy," were I also not afraid of using dirty words. Fortunately, a solution to my cowardly self-image presented itself on the Halloween of my first year of elementary school. I was occupying myself in my bedroom, perhaps knitting a cozy for the thumb I constantly sucked on, when my mother knocked and asked who I wanted to be for Halloween.

"I can pretend to be someone else?" I wondered. It had never occurred to me that I could be any way other than how I was born. It didn't even seem like an option. I stared at her blankly, leaving her to mistake my existential breakdown for a pediatric mental disability.

Part of the problem was that, up until this point, I hadn't made many decisions for myself. Most of them were made for me by my parents. They told me what to do, and I did as I was told. I didn't even get to decide how to answer the phone. I couldn't say "hello," like everyone else in the English-speaking world. My father decided that would be uncouth. Instead, he had me recite a long, scripted response, the way Shakespeare might've answered a phone if he kept one on his nightstand.

"Jamin residence, Michael speaking. Who is this speaking, please?"

I'm not sure why my father wanted his residential phone line to sound like a call center for the March of Dimes, but it must've been important to him. The person on the other end of the line was usually stunned silent, wondering who they had mistakenly called. "I'm sorry," they'd eventually respond. "Can you repeat that?" Then I'd say it again, even faster, completely blurring the words together.

"Jaminresidencemichaelspeakingwhoisthisspeakingplease?" So that's the kind of child I was. Too afraid to answer a phone like everyone else.

"If you could pretend to be anyone ... anyone in the world," my mother repeated, "who would it be?" She was leaning against the doorframe of my bedroom, which was covered in Wacky Pack stickers that were half peeling off. The one for Crust Toothpaste was now attaching itself to her shoulder, clawing its way off the door.

"I don't know. I guess I'd want to be a superhero," I replied.

Given that superheroes are afraid of nothing, it must've felt aspirational to me. A release from the constant fear that seemed to lurk around every corner. Superman was the obvious choice, but even at that young age, I knew to steer away from clichés. Aquaman was a more creative selection. He could talk to fish, which was something I already did to the guppies in my aquarium, and with limited satisfaction. And was that the image of myself that I wanted to project—that I was a strong swimmer? Anything deeper than the kiddie pool scared me, too.

So that left Batman. I liked that he wore a utility belt filled with cool safety gadgets—a solution for every problem. He must've slept so soundly at night, knowing that a canister of shark repellent was never much farther than his penis. The belt my mother dressed me in, on the other hand, was a braided, hippie creation, filled only with peace and sunshine.

I imagined the affectations I'd have to assume dressed as Batman. A fighting stance, or a menacing glare. Either would've been a bluff, and completely out of character for me, but still I was eager to be someone else for a while. Someone brave.

I thought about this during the drive to the local toy store to buy my costume, which was terrifying in its own way. I dreaded sitting in the back seat of our red Volvo station wagon because it always made me nauseous. No one else's car made me want to throw up—just ours. It was because of the way it handled. The suspension wasn't sporty or luxury. It was ipecac. And because the car was stick shift, it was impossible to drive without lurching and jerking. My sister's friend Amelia was the first to throw up in it, christening it like champagne on the hull of a cruise ship. This was during a family trip we took to upstate New York. My sister, Meridith, invited her as a guest, which seemed like a fine idea because Amelia hadn't yet earned the reputation of throwing up on people. But after driving for an hour, Meri and I both noticed her cheeks pulsating—quickly inflating, then deflating in anticipation of an impending eruption.

"Pull over!" pleaded my sister. But asking my father to stop the car was pointless. Unless something was directly inconveniencing him, he would stop for no one.

"We're making good time!" he said, completely oblivious.

"Now, Dad!"

"Yes, now. In an hour, I promise."

"Waaw," replied Amelia, which is the sound vomit makes when it starts to travel from the stomach into the throat. "Waaw!"

And instantly, it was too late. Amelia sprayed the back-seat window in chartreuse chunks of half-digested food. It dripped down the glass onto the window crank, and the acrid smell of curdled cereal quickly filled the car.

"Oh, God," I reacted. "Now *I'm* gonna throw up!"

"No, you're not," responded my sister as my own "waaw" worked its way up my esophagus, threatening to suds down Amelia's vomit with my own.

"Don't. Don't even!" threatened my sister. She was furious.

"I can't help it ... "

"DON'T ... YOU ... DARE!" She dug her nails violently into my bare leg. I shrieked, not in pain, but out of terror.

"Mom, Meri just gave me cancer!!"

Back then, my sister and I were convinced that by digging your nails into someone, you could give them cancer. I think our mother told us that lie to get us to stop fighting with each other, only that backfired. Instead, we just gave each other cancer. And now my own flesh and blood had condemned me to death simply to keep me from throwing up. Luckily for the world, neither of us went into oncology, but that's the kind of fear that I grew up with —that one could get a pinch of cancer.

* * *

On my way to the toy store to pick out a Halloween costume, I kept my head poked out of the car like a dog—just in case I couldn't fight the nausea. From this vantage, it was easy to notice all the Halloween decorations adorning the homes in our neighborhood. Jack-o'-lanterns with angry scowls, life-size ghouls with torn veins poking from their severed limbs ... why was everyone so intent on expressing their worst nightmares? What was fun about fear? I didn't get the appeal. Even nature seemed to be in on the terror of it all, as the cold autumn wind blew rust-colored leaves from the trees. They propped themselves up against the tombstones planted on the front lawns, gasping for their final breath. Scary was in the air.

I was too delicate to handle this kind of imagery. It kept me up at night, and made me dread the horrors that might befall me were I not careful enough. What did I have to do to remain safe? Just give me the protocol and I'll follow it.

At the toy store in Hartsdale Village, I was eager to find the costume section so that I could transform into someone who knew no fear. But the store conspired against me, planting distractions along the way. Even as I snaked my way through the aisles, a model-train set circling the perimeter beckoned for me.

"Come play with me," it called. "Watch me load coal from a factory, then emerge from a tunnel."

But I remained steadfast, even if it meant passing up the opportunity of laying a green army man on the tracks and imagining his panic instead of mine.

"Can I help you?" asked a clerk stocking the shelves.

"Out of my way, old man," I silently shouted as I barreled toward the costume section. He couldn't have been more than 16.

I found the costumes next to the educational toys. It was undesirable real estate for sure, as learning saps the joy out of everything. Back then, costumes were sold in cardboard boxes with cellophane windows so you could view the contents inside. It was almost like looking into a TV set, but in this case I could get as close as I wanted without my mother scaring me about radiation. Just as I was imagining my new life as a Batman, a bright-white glow from the top shelf caught my eye. I had seen that glow before. So calm and untroubled. It belonged to a gentle dead boy who wanted nothing more than human companionship and a response from others that wasn't "ggg-ghost!" It was Casper. I was both shocked and delighted that he was deemed worthy enough to have his own costume, especially given the caliber of company he was in ... with the exception of Aquaman, of course. In my opinion, his powers made him less of a superhero and more of an eccentric with a filthy hobby.

"That one, Mommy!" I shouted. "That's the costume I want."

My mother, eager to be anywhere but a toy store, quickly asked the clerk to fetch a stepladder. Time stood still as I waited for him to return.

"Hurry up, old man!"

When he finally returned, my eyes almost filled with tears as he passed the box down to me. I lifted the lid like an archaeologist opening the Ark of the Covenant, releasing the sacred, toxic fumes that emanated from the cheap, plastic outfit that could've easily been made from a garbage bag.

"You realize I could've easily made this from a garbage bag," said my mother.

"You're crazy!" I barked at her, and I gently carried the costume to the register.

At home, standing on the toilet, I released Casper from his cardboard confines and watched in the mirror as I began my holy transformation. Drawing the elastic string behind my ears, I positioned the stiff plastic mask over my face. It made the world harder to see, but easier to be seen in. Teetering on the edge of the toilet lid, I was no longer Michael—the boy who feared everything. I was now Casper the Friendly Ghost, the boy who others feared.

As a ghost, I could fly, I could walk through walls, and I could do good deeds for others, which, to be quite honest, never occurred to me before putting on the mask. Smiling proudly, I could feel the condensation from my breath pooling against the stiff rim clamped against my chin.

"I'm Casper!" I gurgled in saliva. My face was now wetter than Aquaman's.

The days couldn't pass quickly enough, as I anxiously anticipated my school's Halloween parade. That would be the moment of my big reveal, when my new personality would be bestowed upon the world.

"Why must there be 31 days in October?" I cried. "It's taking too long!"

When Halloween finally arrived, classes were postponed so that all the students could march single file down the main hall. This was for no one's benefit, given that all of us were in the parade and no one was spectating, but still it was majestic. Afterward, we stopped in the gymnasium for a group photo, and I was surprised to discover that I'd been marching behind Adam the whole time. His identity had been concealed behind a Frankenstein mask. He threw his stiff arms toward me, zombie-style, but instead of nervously flinching the way Michael would've, I calmly stepped out of line and pretended to float right past him—Casper-style. Such was the power of the mask.

"Casper!" shouted the photographer. "Get back in line." I paused, appreciative that people were now referring to me by my new name.

"Now, Casper!" he said, pointedly. I didn't like the way he admonished me. It was disrespectful. A lesson is what he needed to learn. It was all I could do to keep from hovering in the air, grabbing him by the collar, and throwing him into the basketball hoop. Yes, the power in me was very strong.

After the photo, I noticed kids starting to take off their masks.

Maybe they were uncomfortable with the sharp holes scraping against their eyelids. Or maybe they just grew bored pretending to be something they weren't. But it ruined the illusion, and it made me mad. If we all wanted to enjoy Halloween, then we all needed to wear our masks. That's the rule. It was bad enough seeing Teddy dressed as some guy named Gerald Ford, but with the plastic disguise resting on top of his head, what was the point of it all? I couldn't be the only one wearing a mask—I'd look stupid. And without my mask, how could I be brave?

I had a similar response almost 44 years later. It was January of 2020, and I was in the San Antonio airport, having just given a talk at a conference. This was two months before the first wave of COVID-19 hit the United States, and even though no one here was really worried about it, fear had already crept into my body, causing me to perform an inventory check on my emergency supplies. Anyone who has visited my garage knows I'm just one spool of razor wire away from being a doomsday prepper. Throw in the whisper of a pandemic, and you've got the makings of a Beijing lockdown. Tucked in one of my emergency bins is a slingshot that will stop an intruder in his tracks ... as long as he holds perfectly still. But airborne pathogens are harder to defend against. My anxiety hasn't turned me into a full-blown germophobe, but for years I've been very conscious about not touching objects crawling with microbes. I look like a gymnast when pulling open public doors, often stretching to reach the very top of the handle, or stooping over to reach the bottom—areas that fewer people are likely to have touched. Sometimes, I'll pretend to make a game out of this, so that onlookers think I'm fun and delightful instead of obsessive-compulsive, like Howard Hughes.

As I walked to the boarding gate, I passed a man in his mid-20s wearing a surgical mask. I suppose he could've been a doctor who had just stepped out of the operating room, but given that he wore flip-flops, baggy shorts, and had a neck tattoo, he didn't strike me as one. A fugitive from an operating room, maybe, running from a detective. He was the first person I saw wearing a paper mask in public, and that made me instantly dislike him. In my mind, he represented the beginning of mass hysteria. Everything I had read suggested that paper masks would do nothing to protect him if he were exposed to the virus. It was more for containing his own infection. I wanted to yell at him that the only person he was protecting was me ... and for some reason, I had a problem with that.

I broke away from the throngs of people marching to their departure gates to buy a snack. I wasn't hungry, but what if I was hungry later? What if the plane got stuck on the tarmac for three hours because of a lightning storm? Or what if the plane took off on time but got diverted to Denver because of an air-traffic-controller strike? It would be wise to have a knapsack full of snacks, just in case.

Before I met Cynthia, I would've grabbed whatever fast food they were selling by the newsstand. But Cynthia is all about herbal, organic, and unprocessed. Now I'm the snob who walks into a mid-end supermarket and thinks, "There's absolutely nothing here to eat!" So at the airport, I spent a good 20 minutes shuttling between vendors, trying to find something that wasn't fried, cheesed, glazed, or hammed. Texas is not the right place for a Californian looking for a low-carb vegan nosh. That left me purchasing a $10 fruit bowl. It actually cost less, but I hesitated as the vendor offered me my change, which certainly was covered with germs. We looked like two sprinters trying to hand off a baton during the 100-meter relay, as I kept pulling my hand farther and farther from hers. Finally, I decided to let her keep her COVID-covered quarters and made a dash to the finish line.

Now, months into a pandemic that has already taken a half-million lives, I think about that masked man on the rare occasions that I venture out of my hermetically sealed home and into a crowded space. "I'm not afraid," I try to convince myself. "I'm not afraid."

It's not fever or chills that puts the fear in me. It's the shortness of breath. The panicked feeling that you can't get enough of the only thing you really need—air. I think about the people hit the hardest, dying alone, without the comfort of their loved ones. Maybe that's the only thing you really need.

Once again, I'm the one with a mask firmly affixed to his face. And when others have them hanging from their neck, I become enraged with indignity. "That's not how masks work!" I want to scream. "If Halloween has taught us anything, it's that we all have to wear them!"

I step cautiously into the public, as if venturing toward the middle of a frozen pond, whose delicate surface could break at any moment. My senses are now always at full alert. Who is walking toward me, and who might catch me from behind? What did I touch, and when did I wash? It's June, and road signs remind us of the presence of plague: CONGRATULATIONS TO THE CLASS OF 2020. They mark the end of lives once freely lived, when children didn't fear death from the breath of their friends. These signs are planted on front lawns like tombstones. Scary is in the air.

The Marisa Disclaimer

Todd was incapable of leaving home without primping in the mirror for 10 minutes. He rubbed styling gel into his hair, tried on this shirt with those pants, then admired his ass like a dog chasing its tail. For the final touch, he released the top two buttons of his shirt, exposing his gold, Italian horn necklace. This, in turn, pointed downward to his crotch, which is really where he wanted to send traffic. Only then was he ready to bid farewell to his true love—the mirror. If Todd was drowning in the ocean, and the lifeboat had room for only one, he would've given up his spot for his reflection.

"Put your shoes on," he yelled toward me. "We're going to the mall."

"Dude, I just got home."

But that wasn't even close to being true. First of all, I wasn't home. I was in the common area of *his* dorm room, not mine. And secondly, I'd been there for hours, with my dirty feet resting on the arm of his couch. This was sophomore year of college, and I spent more time in his room than my own. I liked hanging out with Todd. He was confident and fun, and I studied him with a combination of jealousy and judgment.

"I don't give a shit," he barked. "I need to get a haircut. Let's go."

There was no point in arguing with him. He'd shame me until he got what he wanted, because that's who he was—unapologetically himself. And being so brash and flashy, he had a lot to apologize for. I slipped my sneakers on without tucking my heels in, and stood up.

"You're going like that?" Todd winced, staring at my dirty Stan Smiths, beneath my torn jeans. He grabbed his car keys and headed to the door before I could respond. That was another thing I admired about Todd. He wasn't waiting for answers, because he already had them all.

I liked wearing sneakers. In high school, I wore them every day. They were soft, comfy, and easy to put on. Just jam your foot in, and after a few clumsy steps, the rest of the sneaker would follow. Or not. Tying the laces was optional, but on dressier occasions, I usually made the effort. Some kids didn't even have laces on sneakers, preferring Velcro straps instead. I loved the idea, and surely would've tried a pair if the early adopters hadn't been tagged with the label of "dork." It struck me as odd that Todd always wore dress shoes. They were stiff and uncomfortable. You couldn't run in them, or kick a ball, or even jump in a puddle. True, I had only one memory of ever jumping in a puddle. When I was little, my mother and I were crossing a parking lot on the way to Filene's Basement.

"Why are we going to her basement?" I asked my mother.

"It's a department store."

"And it's in Filene's basement?"

"That's just the name."

"Kind of a bad name for a store, don't you think?"

My mother said nothing, but I didn't let that discourage me.

"If they gave it a better name, wouldn't more people come?"

"Probably."

"So why didn't they give it a better name?"

I was like a dog with a bone back then. When I had a question, I needed the answer right away. It wasn't curiosity so much as it was general uneasiness with sitting in the unknown. My mother probably sensed that, which is why she changed the subject by nudging me toward a puddle of water.

"Go ahead, jump in it."

"Really?"

"Sure!"

She was enticing me to have a little fun—to act my age, which was four. So I jumped in the puddle, sending plumes of water high into the air. It was raw, and primal, and for a moment, I felt powerful. Then, just as I was enjoying this new version of myself, the dirty street water soaked my calves, caking them in oily filth.

"Now I'm wet!" I screamed.

"It's okay," laughed my mother. "You'll change when we get home."

But it wasn't okay. We'd be home later, and I needed this fixed now. I cried about it for the next half-hour while I marinated in filthy puddle juice, waiting in the basement of some lady named Filene. My mother lost patience with me.

"Stop crying like a baby, Michael."

I had no control over that, and I sobbed even more. Living with any kind of discomfort was simply not in my makeup, and it never would be.

Driving with Todd to the mall reminded me of that puddle, because it was almost as uncomfortable. Cold wind blew violently against my face, causing my eyes to water. It was the dead of winter, yet, despite my protests, Todd insisted on keeping the windows to his Pontiac Firebird down. He did this so that people on the street could hear the music he was blasting from the radio, because, of course, they were curious. And this would divert even more attention back to him. I watched as Todd lip-synched to Milli Vanilli, who themselves were lip-synching to someone else. It was like being stuck in a fun-house mirror. The drive was completely unnecessary, as we could've easily walked into town to get a haircut, but Todd wanted to go farther away. The locals, he rightly assumed, were not impressed by the fact that he went to Princeton, and that was his biggest talking point. Once, while at a nearby pizzeria, I watched as he dropped his Princeton credentials to the poor, illiterate clerk behind the counter. She responded, "I go to Princeton, too, jackass."

The mall was far enough away where this wouldn't be a problem. In Todd's mind, the hairstylists there considered us to be real take-home material—as if an Ivy League degree would open doors not just to boardrooms but to bedrooms. When we arrived at the salon, he helped himself to a towel, wrapped it around his neck, and proudly took a chair in front of a three-angled mirror. There, he could admire himself from other perspectives, the way a stranger might admire him. I waited nearby reading *People* magazine.

"Put that fucking thing down!" he whispered. Todd reached into his jacket pocket and tossed me a small paperback written by Friedrich Nietzsche that neither of us would ever read. He thought it would impress girls, so he often carried it as a prop, quoting from it when the occasion called for nihilism.

Todd's hairstylist was an attractive woman in her mid-20s, with a cloud of teased hair hovering above her like a cold front. Watching Todd flirt with her was perplexing. I was amazed at how he could speak to her so comfortably and self-assured. It was a language that I wanted to learn. As she ran her fingers through his hair, they both looked into the mirror, as if they were having sex in a hotel bathroom. It was odd to watch two people converse only through their reflections. It was intimate yet detached. When she was done, she lathered a large puff of mousse in her hands and kneaded it into his scalp, delicately placing each strand of hair exactly as she wanted it. Todd enjoyed this, appreciating a second pair of hands to make him just so. I never considered Todd to be particularly good-looking. As a rugby player, his nose had been broken at least once, but it wasn't his nose that he was awkwardly wedging into every conversation.

"Would you mind taking the sides up just a little?" he asked. "I'm speaking in front of my sociology class tomorrow, and I want to look good."

"Oh, do you go to Trenton State?"

"Princeton," Todd gently corrected.

"Princeton High School?" Oof, that stung.

"University," he said pointedly. If it were me, I would've shivered feverishly with embarrassment, but Todd wasn't bothered. Part of me wished I could be as self-assured as him, but the other part worried what people might think of me if I tried. If only I could get the entire world to sign off on my personality before taking it public.

As we headed toward the parking lot, Todd flashed me a small business card. He turned it over, revealing the hairstylist's phone number written in glitter ink.

"You asked for her number?"

"Yeah. Why not?"

"Well, it didn't seem like you had much in common."

"So?" he responded, almost aggressively, like that was the dumbest thing he'd ever heard. He was choosing a sex partner, not something for a lifetime, like a tattoo. This is what he did. He hit on girls, had sex with them, then never called them back. She was sweet, the hairstylist, and I felt like she deserved better than him. I said nothing, but in that moment I felt superior to Todd. While he was looking for a quantity of women, I was looking for something much better. Quality. Someone to share a meaningful, intimate relationship with. That's what separated me from Todd. I was deep.

"Let's go through Neiman Marcus," blurted Todd.

"Why?"

He nodded toward a beautiful woman in her early 30s who was displaying a bottle of men's cologne. She was tall in her high-heel shoes, which only made her more intimidating. A few strands of brown hair intentionally dangled across her cheek, like someone hadn't completely removed the gift-wrapping from her face. Considering how hot she was, I was shocked there wasn't a line of men waiting to be sprayed by her. Todd saw this woman as the perfect candidate to hit on, because her job required her to be verbally responsive to people like us. It was almost mean of him, I thought, to keep her hostage like that.

"I'll try some," he called off to the saleswoman, walking toward her with long, confident strides. I watched with trepidation.

"But just a small spray," he continued. "I have to get back to Princeton, where I have a seminar on the Fundamentals of Neuroscience. It's a tight room, and I don't want to overwhelm the other Princeton students."

Wow. Princeton got two mentions in one speech. That was like spiking a football, picking it up, and spiking it again. But I guess it worked, because now she was touching him, straightening his collar. Her hands were literally on his body, and I couldn't believe it.

"Do you want to try some, too?" she said, looking in my direction. Todd smiled, as if he were gifting her to me.

"Um, okay," I stepped forward, regretting that I was wearing a ratty T-shirt instead of something with a collar. Something that she could grab onto.

She squirted two large clouds and nodded for me to walk through them, which I did, like a stripper bursting through a curtain of beads. "Hello, boys. You can call me Tanqueray." I sauntered, to soak in every moment of her attention. But something was wrong, and foolishly, I didn't try to hide it.

"I don't smell anything," I said. Immediately, the sparkle evaporated from her eyes. It was such a dumb thing to say, given that I was effectively calling her out. What was to be gained by that?

"It's a sophisticated blend for mature gentlemen," she said, forcing a smile. I stared at her blankly, then back to Todd, who had turned his head away in embarrassment.

"That means you're not ready for it," she added.

"That means I'm not *ready* for it?"

"Maybe one day."

Her blue eyes stared through me, condescendingly. They were beautiful, which is why I didn't want to look away, but still, I fumed.

"That means I'm not ready for it. What kind of bullshit is that?" This was me, back in Todd's car. I repeated her words over and over, as if there was something in them that I missed, the same way there was something in the cologne that I missed.

"Who does she think she is?!" I snapped.

"She's too hot for you, anyway," replied Todd.

"Maybe the problem is her shitty perfume smells like New Jersey tap water."

"Smelled good to me," said Todd, laughing. Then Milli Vanilli played, escorting us back to campus.

* * *

At the bottom of my closet, behind my laundry basket, was a shoebox. Unlike most shoeboxes found in college dorm rooms, mine wasn't filled with pot or porn. It actually contained shoes. They were cordovan penny loafers my mother bought for my high-school graduation, even though my long gown would've easily concealed my sneakers. I brought them to my dorm room at the beginning of freshman year, in case I needed to need to wear them when I graduated college. But clearly there was a need for them now. I stuffed my hands into them, as if I had no idea how shoes were supposed to be worn, and held them before me. They felt cold and stiff, as if they'd been taken off a corpse. I thought about Todd, and I thought about the woman at the department store. They both made me feel less than—like an amateur man. It made me want to change.

I slid my feet into my shoes and tried to admire them. They didn't look right with torn jeans, so I reached into my dresser for a pair of khakis. It still had the tags on them, and I held them at arm's length because we both hated each other. Then I invited my ridiculous brown sweater into the conversation, and boy did it have lots to say—none of it flattering. There was nothing about this look that I liked, and I recoiled from my reflection. Did I really have to be this guy?

I exited my dorm room and stepped lightly, uncomfortable with this new arrangement with myself. But as I walked down the corridor to my Contemporary English class, something changed. I was struck by the sound my shoes made on the marble floors. Unlike my sneakers, the leather soles of my shoes made a satisfying tap-tappity-tap. It was like they were heralding my presence, and I appreciated the fanfare. Going upstairs, it changed into more of "shushing" sound. Like sandpaper. Shh. Shh. Shh. Now my shoes were trying to quiet everyone down so I could say something important. It was so dramatic. No wonder Todd wore shoes.

It must've been my shoes' idea to attend the university orchestra that Saturday evening, as I wouldn't have come up with anything that sophisticated on my own. It was held in Richardson Auditorium, a concert hall on campus. With its steep, gabled ceiling and Romanesque features, me and my penny loafers fit right in. I met Todd in the balcony, and I was certain he'd have something complimentary to say about my new look. Maybe a double-take and a hearty nod of approval. Instead, he barely took notice and said nothing. I even rested one ankle over my knee to make it more obvious. I had to remind myself that I was doing this for me. Me and only me. And all the girls that would soon appreciate this version of me, like the fine wine that I was aging into.

Before the concert started, the musicians tuned up. They played scales and random notes. The cacophony sounded horrible. I imagine they could have done this in unison to sound melodic, but they did it separately, so that when the music actually started, it sounded beautiful in comparison. It was a simple case of before vs. after, and I realized that dressing like a schlub my whole life might actually have been a stroke of genius. Look at me before, and look at me now!

I barely listened to the concert. Come on, it was classical music. Instead, my eyes scanned the audience, searching for anyone that might be admiring me. Anyone at all. No one? Not a soul? But that's when things shifted. I went from hoping to be seen ... to seeing. And what I saw was perfection. She was sitting right on the stage, playing what looked to be a big violin. It was hard to make out her features from so far away, but she was small, with blonde, wavy hair that occasionally brushed her shoulders as she swayed to the music. She did this with her eyes closed, as if the only way she could truly understand something was by feeling it in her soul. It was profound and exactly the way I deserved to be understood. I was surprised that I'd never seen someone this amazing before on campus, and proud that I had willed her into existence, simply by wearing my shoes. I watched, love-stricken, as her fingers danced upon the neck of her big violin and her magnificent breasts heaved against the bout from—

"It's called a 'cello,'" interrupted Todd.

"I know what it's called, Todd. I'm not an idiot."

I watched, love-stricken, as her fingers danced upon the neck of her big violin and her magnificent breasts heaved against the —

"Well, then you should call it a 'cello.'"

"Yes, thank you, Todd. So helpful."

What would it take for me to be the big violin cradled between her thighs? I had the shoes, I had the sweater, and I had the khakis. All I needed now was the introduction. And the nerve to open my mouth. That last part would be hard.

In the lobby, once the concert let out, I pushed through the crowds, trying to find her. I hoped she might be standing at the door, thanking patrons as they left, or posing for photographs. Something glamorous like that. I had to see her up close—this marvelous invention of mine—and hear her laugh and feel her presence. I never found her, though, and for that I was grateful. I wouldn't have known what to do if I did, so I was spared. Now I could focus on the search, which would be futile, and more my speed. By the staircase I noticed a program. It had been trampled on, with faint bootprints dirtying the cover. Maybe I could figure out her name. I picked the program off the floor, which made me feel poor and desperate, like a scavenger. It was something the old me would've done. Toward the back of the program was a list of all the orchestra members sorted by instrument. With that as a clue, I was able to narrow her name down to one of three choices, and I decided that she must be Marisa. There was really no reason to assume this, but that's the name I found most attractive, so that's what I made her. I willed it so. I imagined watching TV with Marisa in her dorm room, my arm around her shoulder while I lightly stroked her ponytail. I'd seen my friend Wyatt do that with his girlfriend, and it seemed so gentle and intimate. It had never occurred to me that a girl might let you do that until I saw Wyatt do it. That's something I never would have learned from Todd.

I spent the next few weeks crisscrossing the campus, constantly on the lookout for a blonde girl wheeling a big violin case. As much as you'd think a person like that would stand out, I never saw her. I came up with theories as to why I didn't. Like maybe she had two big violins: one in her dorm room, and another at her rehearsal space. Or maybe she traveled only at night. That would certainly make her more mysterious, which I found appealing. Or maybe she had a boyfriend who shuttled her big violin for her. As unlikely as that scenario sounded, it filled me with jealousy.

Then, one day, while sliding my plastic, orange tray along the metal railings of the lunch counter, I overheard two girls talking about orchestra rehearsal. My head swiveled like an owl after hearing a baby mouse squeak deliciously for the first time. It was silent, the way my head spun, but not at all subtle. One of the girls was an acquaintance of mine. A friend of a friend, really. The other was pretty, with blonde, wavy hair and radiant skin that could barely contain her love for me. Her nose had a slight bump on it, which made her even cuter. I was convinced she was Marisa. Beautiful, perfect Marisa. I wanted to start our relationship off on the right foot, so I stalked her to the salad bar.

Hiding behind the sneeze guard, I watched while pretending to grab at the mini-corns with a plastic tong. They always looked so delightful, mini-corns. Tiny and cute. But once tasted, they inevitably disappointed, with their soggy blandness. What if

Marisa was like the mini-corn that was flailing at the tip of my tongs? Good from afar, but far from good. No, that couldn't be the case. I mean, her talent alone vaulted her to the level of goddess. I threw caution to the wind and added a mini-corn to my plate. Bold decision.

The girls were now talking about their chemistry homework. Something something-organic. There may have been mention of molecules, who knows—I was burning a hole in my new girlfriend's head with my super-laser-beam eyes. Finally, I heard the other one say the magic word. She called her "Marisa."

"Wait," I interrupted, without thinking. "You play big violin in the orchestra!"

"Yes, I do!" she smiled, with a shimmer in her eyes that can be found only in accomplished cellists. It takes years of practice and sacrifice to have that shimmer in your eyes. Experienced violinists might come close, but it's not the same. You have to be a cellist. I guess you could say I was smitten.

I began my courtship of Marisa with a couple of lies. First, I told her how much I enjoyed the concert, which wasn't really true. I just enjoyed watching her. Then I told her how much I appreciated classical music, which definitely wasn't true. I didn't tell her about my shoes and how I just recently started wearing them, but the thought came into my mind. I chased it away because I feared that just mentioning shoes would remind her that she had feet and was free to walk away. I considered positioning myself between her and the table, where our mutual friend was waiting, just to make her escape harder. But after a few minutes, it didn't seem necessary. I got the feeling that Marisa was enjoying me. As she spoke, I caught myself staring at my shoes—these magical, transformational shoes of mine.

Todd had a rule of always being the first to end the conversation when you meet a new girl, just to keep her off-balance. He claimed that's why he didn't ask the woman selling cologne in the department store for her number. I didn't want to do that. Over Marisa's shoulder, I could see our friend waiting impatiently, so I asked if we could have dinner sometime. Maybe Friday night. I said it as if I was taking her to a fancy restaurant, instead of just meeting her at the dining hall for a meal our parents already paid for. Using all my brainpower, I willed her to say yes.

"It's a deal," she said, and I relaxed my brow.

* * *

Sitting through my phonetics-and-phonology class was torture. I signed up for it because it was supposed to be a gut. That is to say, an easy class to lighten my schedule. That was false advertising, just a lie that someone invented and I naïvely believed. Because of that, I was now trying to understand glottal stops and ambidental articulations, as if that would somehow change my life, when all I really needed was a pair of shoes. It was agonizing, thinking about Marisa roaming free on the campus, an easy target for anyone better than me. I stared at the clock on the wall, angry that Friday evening couldn't drag its dumb, lazy ass to me soon enough, and I really didn't give a shit what a fricative was.

When Friday finally arrived, I found Marisa right where she said she'd be—standing outside the dining hall. The back door to the kitchen opened, releasing a cloud of steam, as if she were emerging from a dream. As I approached, we raced to see who'd smile first, and I think it was a tie.

"You'll love this place," I joked, even though we both knew the food there was terrible. Then we handed the attendant our meal cards and walked toward the service counter. Sliding our orange trays one behind the other was awkward, and I wanted to move past the "getting to know each other" part and jump to the part where I lovingly stroked her ponytail. It was hard for me to keep the conversation going while simultaneously deliberating over the two meal options. I chose the *penne arrabbiata* because saying it out loud made me sound sophisticated. Far more sophisticated than just "the chicken." How's that supposed to impress anyone?

We found a table on a small riser that the school sometimes used as a stage when the dining hall was converted for special events. Sitting there with her made me feel important. Center stage with Marisa, just as it was when I first saw her. As she spoke about the classes she was taking, the clubs she belonged to, and the high school she graduated from, I allowed my mind to wander. I was no longer sitting with Marisa. I was back at the mall, pitying Todd for not being as enlightened as I was. All his rules and posturing were just so sad. If there were a Hall of Fame for 19-year-olds reaching maturity exceptionally fast, I surely would've been inducted. Of course, I'd graciously thank Todd in my acceptance speech, but I'd say it so that everyone could detect my sarcasm. I'd practice a few times the night before, to get the tone just right.

"You want to hit the street?" I asked Marisa, after she seemed to finish her thought, whatever it was. "The street" was what they called the party scene at Princeton. It's where you could find cheap beer on tap, as well as deafening dance music. It seemed like the perfect place to bring a special lady.

"With you? Nah," she joked, before adding, "Just kidding." I laughed, and we grabbed our coats.

It was cold outside, and I crammed my hands inside the pockets of my leather bomber jacket. I always felt cool wearing it, even though it now clashed horribly with my cordovan penny loafers. In retrospect, I looked like someone transitioning through something—one foot in each phase, both of them disastrous.

Marisa looped her hand through my arm as we walked, and it gave me pause. Something about it felt unearned, almost artificial, like the conversation Todd had with the hairstylist in the mirror. But I said nothing and just continued, as if this was how Marisa and I always walked—her hand wrapped around my arm. Hers was the same hand that only a few weeks earlier had pulled life into a cello with a bow. Or was it the hand that pressed the strings along the neck? What difference did it make? I was now with Marisa.

The party was inside a stately old mansion where the upperclassmen ate. The grandeur of the oversize wooden door quickly gave way to a wall of loud hip-hop music, the bass of which made the stone foundation shudder. The leather soles of my shoes stuck to the floors, where spilled beer hadn't yet been mopped up, and I took Marisa's hand as I pulled her though the room, which was humid from the sweat of adolescents dancing tightly next to each other. A half-dozen jocks chugged beer from a funnel, because drinking from a can was too childish. Onlookers cheered them on, and I cheered as well, because being with Marisa wasn't enough. I wanted others to know that I was with her—and that I'd earned the affection of this wonderfully talented, beautiful woman by being true to my values. Values that were way more valuable than Todd's values.

We found some space by a window opposite the coatroom. By now we weren't talking. The music was too loud, so we just screamed at each other, which is what two people in love do. A drunken party-goer passed, nudging Marisa's shoulder and splashing beer all over her top. I was pissed at him for ruining our moment.

"I'm good," she waved at him. I was impressed at how she responded. Not flustered or annoyed. Just taking it in stride. Tolerance was a quality that I lacked, and I admired that in her. It felt reassuring. We could be good together, me and Marisa, the envy of all our friends. She blotted at her shirt with a napkin I found on the windowsill, and when the guy was far enough away, she leaned toward me and said, "I'm going to push that jerk down a flight of stairs." I laughed. Pretty *and* a sense of humor. What a catch.

"Just kidding," she then added.

That part struck me as odd. "Just kidding." It was the second time she said it. Obviously, she was just kidding, so why the disclaimer? Did she think that I didn't understand what humor was? Whatever. It was minutiae. No need to get bogged down in little things when we had our love to focus on.

"So when's your next concert?" I shouted to her, as if she were standing at the opposite end of a football field.

"Don't ask. So much rehearsal. I'm thinking of joining the crew team and using my cello as an oar."

Again I laughed. Marisa was great. And her heart was as big as her violin.

"Just kidding," she then added.

Wait. Okay, stop. I knew she was just kidding. We all knew. Was there any expectation that she might actually throw her cello into Lake Carnegie? I turned my head from her so that she couldn't read my expression. I needed a moment to settle and collect my thoughts. I stared out the window, straining to make out the people on the lawn below. They were arguing, or maybe they were laughing. Sometimes it looks the same. My eyes refocused to Marisa's reflection in the window. She was looking across the room, hoping to spot someone she knew. Marisa's face was so soft and warm—almost innocent. I liked looking at Marisa this way, with distance. It reminded me of when I first saw her, high from the balcony of Richardson Auditorium. That is to say, when she was perfect.

"You okay?" she asked. "You got quiet like a mouse." I

nodded. Maybe I was being too hard on her. She was perceptive and in tune with my feelings. It's rare to find someone this sweet and considerate.

"Just kidding," she added. Oh, fuck. Now that one took me by complete surprise. It was perplexing. There wasn't even any pretense of kidding. Where was the joke? Where was the kidding part? Show it to me! I had to rethink our relationship. Break it off with her before things got serious. I braced myself, then looked into her eyes, but they were big and brown, and they glowed when she smiled. I was at a complete loss, and so I did the worst thing I could possibly ever do. I leaned in and kissed her. My eyes were wide open as I did it, certainly from shock. "What the fuck are you doing?!" they must've screamed. She didn't hear those screams, however, because she kissed me back. Now, despite my confusion, Marisa and I were dating.

For the next few weeks, we ate dinner together, we sat on the couch together, and we had sex together. I had gotten what I wanted: the beautiful musician from the orchestra. And Marisa got what she wanted, which was the opportunity to repeat "just kidding" like she was Oprah giving away cars. "And *you* get just kidding ... and *you* get just kidding!" This was a problem. I had jumped into a puddle, and now my feet were wet and dirty, and I couldn't ignore it. I simply could not tolerate the discomfort.

I needed to talk to someone. Someone who would sympathize with my situation and encourage me to do the selfish thing, no matter who it might hurt. Someone like Todd. He was a lone wolf and pragmatic about relationships. He'd give me the green light to just break things off with Marisa and move on with my life. Thank God for Todd.

"I don't get what the big deal is," he said while folding red bikini briefs from his laundry basket. "Are you banging her?"

"Yes."

"Is she getting clingy?"

"No."

"Does she want you to do girl shit with her?"

"No."

"Does she stink? Is she gross? Is she skanky?"

"No!"

"Then what the hell's the problem?"

"I told you. She says 'just kidding' a lot."

"So, ignore it."

'I can't ignore it, Todd. I can't! That's not in my nature."

"It's not like you're so perfect yourself," he replied.

"Yes, but there's room for only one damaged person in our relationship, and I got here first!"

Todd pulled a satin sheet from his laundry basket and tucked it under his chin while he doubled it. An expensive pair of women's lace panties dropped out.

"Look, man, I don't know what your deal is," he said wearily. "You kinda sound like a chick to me, and it's getting old. I think you need to accept that she's a human being and shut the fuck up." He rolled the lace panties into a ball, clearly something special that his hookup had worn for his benefit, and threw them into the garbage.

Todd could be a real dick sometimes, just not when you needed him to be.

* * *

I steeled myself as I walked to Marisa's dorm room. Late afternoon was turning into evening, and the path lights were just coming on. The campus was deceptive this way, with hints of yellow trailing off into the darkness. Once again, I stepped lightly as I made my way downhill, the leather soles of my shoes providing little grip on the wet flagstones. I was going to be okay, though. Even though Todd wasn't helpful, my conversation with him was. It convinced me more than ever that I didn't want to be like him. That I wouldn't treat women the way he did. I'd treat them with respect and dignity. That's what I decided to do as I greeted Marisa at her door. I took her hand and gently said there was something we needed to talk about. I told her she had a nervous habit that she probably wasn't even aware of. I needed to point it out, not to hurt her feelings, but so that we could both move forward and grow closer, because that's what mature people do.

Just kidding. That would've been awkward. Instead I simply hid from her, like a coward, and never called again. The woman selling cologne at the department store had been right about me all along. I wasn't ready for it.

Fourth and Long

"Get dressed. We're going to the Jets game today!" shouted my father.

He didn't say it with the excitement of a sports fan. No, his voice was full of dread, like he was going in for exploratory bowel surgery to find his car keys after having looked everywhere else for them. The only reason we were attending the game was because his boss gave him the tickets, and my father didn't want to seem ungrateful. So now he had to schlep to the Meadowlands and sit on a cold, plastic slab for three hours.

"Can I see the tickets?" I asked him a half-dozen times on the ride there.

"Not until we're in our seats."

Despite the fact that he didn't want to go to the game, my father still guarded the tickets like they could get him through a Nazi checkpoint.

"Can you believe how expensive these things are?" he complained, "What a rip-off. You see the game better on TV, and it's free!" He pushed his way through the crowd, with me struggling to keep up.

"Stay close," he said as he headed down the gate to our seats. "If I lose you, your mother won't let me hear the end of it." He said this to the eight-year-old girl behind him. I was still stuck on the escalator.

We sat in our seats, waiting for the stadium to fill, and my father's attitude slowly shifted. He started waxing nostalgic, telling football stories from his own youth, where his athletic prowess was nothing short of Olympic. In most of these tales, he humiliated his chief rival. That is to say, his brother, who was equally unathletic, several years his junior, and overweight. While my father was inducting himself into the Hall of Fame, I used this as an opportunity to leaf through the program we picked up at the concession stand.

"What's the difference between offsides and false start, Dad?"

He had no idea, but was eager to pass down some kind of masculine knowledge to his only son. So he reached deep into the knapsack full of snacks that my mother had prepared for us. There, next to a thermos full of hot cocoa, was a bottomless can of bullshit, which he generously shared with me.

"There are two sides to the stadium, right? If a team is offsides, one side of the stadium sees more action than the other, and that's not fair." His explanation was so made up it was practically science fiction.

From my father, I inherited both his ignorance of the sport and his lack of athletic skill. This would later become an issue in gym class, when I was routinely chosen second-to-last for whatever game we were playing that day. Last-place honors usually fell to the transfer student from India who didn't understand English. There's no faster way to learn a language than having someone scream "Duck, Pranav!" before getting smacked in the head by a dodgeball. I tried not to care so much about it, but children can be cruel, and the derision I constantly faced made me dislike who I was. A nerd. A dork.

A half-hour before the game's national anthem, a lone player jogged to the 50-yard line. This was the punter, and he wore a single bar across his face mask, which made his helmet look like it came with a scoop of ice cream inside. He seemed so out of place standing in the middle of the field, far from the rest of the team. He pulled a few blades of grass from the turf to check which way the wind was blowing. Then he adjusted a little towel tucked under his belt. Then he licked his fingers, like they'd been dipped in barbecue sauce. There was so much ritual to appreciate, and it was all so delicate and demure. It made me think of my mother checking her makeup in the mirror. Swinging his long leg into the air, this man looked less like a football player and more like one of the cheerleaders. But when he dropped the football in front of him and kicked it, all that changed. With such force, he sent that ball high into the air with a tight, clean spiral, where it paused at its apex before screaming toward the end zone. A brown leather rainbow.

"Do you think he can kick it out of the stadium?" I asked my father, in complete awe.

"As long as he doesn't break my windshield, I don't give a shit what he does." He was now holding binoculars to his eyes, looking everywhere but the field. "Whaddya know! There's an exit that'll take us even closer to our car."

On fourth down, all my interest went to the punter. This is when real football fans booed. The punter represented capitulation. It meant that the offense had failed. But I didn't boo. I applauded like a toddler watching clowns spill out of a tiny car. "Yay! Do it again!" So what if the opposing team ran this punt back for a touchdown? Look how magnificent it was. Field-goal kickers didn't kick spirals. Their kicks go end over end, making them look like a mistake. But a punt had that spiral and the artistry. I realized that the punter was part of the team, but also apart from the team. He didn't need to be violent or even physical. He was a different kind of athlete—one that maybe I could be.

When we returned home, I decided I'd try this punting thing myself. I found a football in the closet that my well-meaning but sadly mistaken grandfather had given to me as a birthday gift, hoping that I would be athletic. No doubt he had given a similar gift to my father when he was a boy, disappointed with that outcome as well.

I brought the ball to the front lawn and mimicked the stance of a professional punter. I visualized the motions, then shushed the deafening roar of the crowd that I was also imagining.

"Please, everyone! I'm trying to concentrate."

I took a few steps, dropped the ball, and swung my leg as hard as I could.

In an instant, I learned something absolutely crucial about punting. If you kick the ball incorrectly, you'll collapse to the ground in pain as shrieks of agony arise from deep within your lungs, ricocheting off your baby teeth before pushing your lifeless tongue out of your mouth like a wind sock at an airfield.

That's the scorching pain I felt as my dreams of being an athlete blew into the autumn sunset. And that was the last time I ever punted a football—until my junior year of high school, when the ball cried out for me again.

I was watching Monday Night Football as background noise to my Monday night homework, when suddenly I noticed that the crowd had stopped cheering. I looked up from my books to discover that the punter had just taken the field, and the silence came from the collective "Who gives a shit?" Well, I gave a shit. At least enough for me to put down my assignment for a minute. Back then, I spent a lot of time lost in textbooks. It was easier to struggle with precalculus than it was to confront the emotional pain I was going through. Everyone in my family was going through it, and none of us had any clue how to deal with it. And so we all just suffered.

I watched as the punter sent the ball flying into the stratosphere. The camera cut to the receiver as he waited impatiently for it to return to Earth, and the fact that the punter made a real athlete seem so helpless made me smile. That's when I decided to revisit this dream of mine from my childhood—to be something other than the nerdy kid who lived only in books.

Every day after school, I'd stand in front of my home and spend an hour or so punting. Attempting to kick the ball over our steep roof seemed like a good idea. If it cleared the roof, great. If not, the ball would bounce back to me, maybe bringing a shingle with it on the way down. Ordinarily, this is something my father would've punished me for, but my parents were divorced now, and my home wasn't his home anymore. Things changed when he moved out. My parents fought a lot, so our house was often filled with yelling, and crying, and doors slamming. Their divorce wasn't entirely unwelcome, but I was surprised at what it left in its wake. Silence. With my father gone and my sister in college, it was just me and my mom. After school, I'd come home to an empty house, a shell of what it once was, with only the creaks of the hardwood floors to fill the stillness. Those little noises made me uneasy. I'd grab a snack from the kitchen, usually a Hostess Fruit Pie, then tiptoe past the living room and back out the front door. Along the way there, I shut all the doors behind me, so that the space would feel smaller and I'd feel bigger. This was the in-between time, before my mother would return from work, exhausted from the day behind her and weary for the one yet to come. It was better to be outside during this time of silence, pretending to be someone I wasn't, punishing my house with the smack of a football.

What started as a distraction turned into a daily meditation. I'd lose myself in the simple, repetitive motion of punting a football. *Head down, drop it flat, follow through.* There was no room for other thoughts, and there were many of them. Instead, I repeated these simple instructions to attain the elusive perfect punt, which I hunted as if it held the secret to inner peace.

When the neighbors drove by, they slowed down, wondering what I was up to. It made me self-conscious, like they knew I had no business holding a football. But after a few weeks, I became another fixture on the street, like a lamppost or a fire hydrant, and they drove right by. Even in the cold of winter when the snow blocked the road, I cleared a narrow path with a shovel so that I could continue punting.

"That's the kid who won't go inside," I imagined them saying. "Why won't he go inside?"

When I wasn't punting, I was looking for ways to get better. But this was long before the Internet, and instruction was hard to find. I watched high-school football teams play, but their punters looked nothing like the professionals on TV. These were simply kids recruited from other positions, who just kicked with brute force. They lacked grace and intention. Surprisingly, I found what I was looking for one day after school, when I wandered into a practice session for the gymnastics team. One of the sophomore girls was rehearsing her floor routine. She had just done one of those cartwheels without using her hands—the kind that looks like an accident. It made me want to shout, "Hey, you forgot to use your hands!" After she came out of her flip, she threw her leg toward the ceiling, and I gasped, "Look how high she can kick!" Put a helmet on her and she looked no different than a punter.

"Excuse me," I thought of saying, "How do you do that?"

But that would've required conversing with a 16-year-old in a leotard, and I was certain she didn't want to share that level of intimacy with me. Instead, I watched her from the bleachers, ignoring her occasional looks of revulsion.

"I'm not creeping on you," I whispered. "I'm just admiring your thighs as they gently brush against your cheekbones."

In the privacy of my home, I began a daily stretching routine so that I, too, could acquire the flexibility of a teenage girl wearing a one-piece. I forced myself to touch my toes with my palms, shrieking as my hamstrings threatened to snap. I pushed through the pain, though, which is very uncharacteristic of me, and over the following weeks I began to notice major improvements. I could now swing my foot completely over my head. At full extension, I looked like I belonged on top of a music box.

One Sunday morning, while watching football on TV, I saw a punter jog onto the field wearing only one shoe. The announcer mentioned that he kicked barefoot because it gave him more control.

"Now that's a real man," I thought. "Even if he is just a punter." I ran outside, removed my right shoe, and stood poised to try it myself. Moments later, lying face down on the street with gravel stuck to my forehead, I made an another important realization: if you're barefoot and you don't strike the ball perfectly, you'll vomit in agony. For weeks I continued punting without a shoe, because it taught me how to hit the ball correctly. It hurt, but it's what I needed to get better.

By the fall of my senior year in high school, my punting had improved quite a bit. I wasn't terrible anymore. I was just bad. My kicks didn't look anything like that Jets player I admired all those years ago. They looked like something I would do. I decided I needed formal instruction from someone who actually knew how to punt. The obvious place to look for help was the football team, but the idea of trying out seemed ridiculous. I was a geek, not an athlete. When I walked down the hallways, girls would shout, "Stop looking at me, you idiot." Maybe they never said it out loud, but in my mind, that's what they were thinking. And that's how I saw myself.

Up until that point, I'd kept my punting a secret from everyone. Secrets, of course, have a way of leaking out, and when my best friends discovered that I was trying out for the varsity football team, they greeted the news the way best friends are supposed to —by mocking me.

"How could you possibly think you're a football player? Whenever we play at lunch, we say horrible things about you. We say them out loud. We make sure you hear them!"

They saw me as a fraud. A nerd trying to re-invent himself as an athlete. Most surprised was my father. Since the divorce, I'd only see him once or twice a week, and he was aware that he was missing the last few months of my childhood. Had he already missed so much that now I was a football player? The truth is, my friends were right. I *did* want to be someone else. Someone who didn't have to console his crying mother all the time. Someone who didn't feel guilty for not visiting his father more often. Someone who could send a football far away.

If my friends thought I was crazy, the reception I got from the football team was even more hostile. Many of the players teased me, and some wanted to beat the shit out of me for not knowing my place. At tryouts, not even the head coach couldn't understand why I wanted to be the punter, so he made a counter-offer.

"How about punter and backup tight end? That could be fun."

But I stood firm. It was punter and nothing else. What was the point? I didn't want to get tackled or hurt. I just wanted that perfect kick. "Make sure there's extra padding in this guy's helmet," he joked, and everyone laughed. I smiled politely, fully aware that I didn't belong.

During practice, while my teammates exhausted themselves with drills, I punted in an adjacent field, kicking a ball, then jogging to get it, then kicking it back. The same one ball, over and over, for hours. Sometimes I'd stop to admire an oddly shaped cloud, or just smell the freshly cut grass as the evening wind blew in. But it was the uniform that I remember most. The bulky shoulder and thigh pads protecting me like armor. The bars on my face mask hiding who I really was.

Even though my father never understood the joy of watching football, he still came to all my games. He'd sit patiently in the bleachers, cheering only when I took the field.

"You really crushed a few of those kicks," he'd say after the game, over lunch at our local diner. That wasn't the case at all. But it was nice to see that, despite the divorce, he was still carrying around the bottomless can of bullshit my mother packed for him all those years ago. Because we always lost, he thought it was necessary to console me—like the final score was somehow tied to my identity. I couldn't have cared less about the score. It was never about that.

By season's end, I was no closer to my goal. But I couldn't quit either. Not after all the hard work I had put into it. I was accepted to Princeton, which had a football team. It's not exactly Texas A&M, but it is college level. Division I. The players were a lot bigger and stronger than the kids in high school, and most had been recruited to play there. On the first week of school, I tried out as a walk-on. I didn't even know what a walk-on was until one of the recruited players sardonically said, "Oh, you're a walk-on." I wore my oddly mismatched shoes so that people would recognize me as a punter and not some other skilled position that I had no business playing. Part of me was expecting to be thrown off the field, which I would've been at peace with. Then it would've been someone else's decision for me to give up and not my own.

The special-teams coach gave me a tryout. He was an older man, maybe in his late 60s, with a full head of white hair. He looked at me dismissively, which was fair, given that I was six feet tall but only weighed 155 pounds. I didn't look like a football player—I looked like an asparagus tip. The coach handed me a few balls, and he watched as I punted them. I kicked them okay, but certainly not well enough to get a spot on the team. After a few minutes, he motioned for me, and I returned to his side, where he tried to talk some sense into me.

"We already have a punter. You'd be behind him."

I nodded, in full agreement that I was barely good enough to be second string.

"You might not even travel to the away games. So half the season you wouldn't play."

"I'm okay with that." And I was. I really didn't care about that at all.

Rather than waste time arguing with me, he glanced at his clipboard and assigned me a locker in a far-off corner. The location was perfect.

I was surprised to learn how well the college-football players were treated. They provided us with free cleats, and at the end of every practice, they even washed our uniforms, although mine never got dirty. I could spend a week in mine, and it would still be cleaner than those jumpsuits scientists wear to build satellites. I even got my own football jacket. It was black with orange trim, and my name was embroidered on the front. It was strange to see it there.

My daily routine as a college-football player was even cushier than it was in high school. It was as if I was on vacation. I'd grab a bag of balls, wander off to the practice field, and turn my worries off for a few hours. *Head down, drop it flat, follow through.*

One day, the head coach decided that the party was over. They were short a player at practice and needed an extra body for a drill. He yelled at me from across the field.

"You! You're tight end now!" I was impressed that the coach realized I was part of the team, and not some 10-year-old trick-or-treating in a football costume. But still, I wasn't keen on participating in his little scrimmage. And why was everyone trying to get me to play tight end? Wasn't that kind of insulting to tight ends?

I ran toward the huddle.

"Today!" he shouted, not realizing I was sprinting at full speed.

This was first time I had ever been in a huddle, and it was tighter than I expected. Lots of guys sweating, cursing, spitting. Honestly, it was a little gross.

"I'm not really sure what I'm supposed to be doing," I said to the group.

The quarterback pointed to a linebacker and told me to block him. "You mean, like, from my memory?" It was a fun little *bon mot* for my gridiron compatriots to lighten the mood, and it was met with silence.

The linebacker I was assigned to hit was a guy named Darnell, and he was built like Apollo's better-looking brother. My locker wasn't far from his, so I'd often see him without his shirt. Chiseled abs. Rock-hard pecs. Laying a hit on a guy twice my size seemed like a terrible idea, but the quarterback wouldn't listen to reason.

"What if I just run a passing route over the middle? You can throw the ball at my head like a metal duck in a carnival game."

The quarterback yelled "hike," and sensing no alternative, I quickly reset my mind from "learned helplessness" to "angry determination." Despite the fact that I had no business being there, I didn't want to embarrass myself. I raced downfield like a missile seeking its target, ready to destroy. There was Darnell, just a few yards in front of me.

"Two seconds to impact!" shouted a voice in my head.

If I caused Darnell serious injury, it was the coach's fault for putting me in.

"One second to impact!"

Goodbye, Darnell. Please forgive me.

I was about to obliterate this beautiful statue of flesh and blood, this gift from God, when, with the lightest touch, Darnell extended his arms and gently swatted me away. He did it without thinking, the way a horse's tail might brush away a fly. I was amazed at how gentle he was. People handle Waterford crystal more roughly. I fell to the ground, tumbling and tumbling, eventually rolling to a stop somewhere near the goalpost.

"Wow!" I thought. "So this is what it's like to get a uniform dirty."

Having easily dodged my block, Darnell went on to tackle the running back for a two-yard loss. When I dusted myself off and returned to the huddle, the coach was furious.

"I told you to put a hit on him!"

I was shocked at the coach's reprobation, especially after how hard I tried, and barked back, "And I told you I'm not a football player, you fucking idiot!"

No, I didn't actually say that. What I really said was somewhat less heroic. I'm not proud of this, but I may have apologized for getting my uniform dirty.

Furious, the coach kicked me off the gridiron, and I could hear my teammates snicker as I slinked back to the small punting field, where the fairies and woodland creatures greeted my safe return. There, I hid for a few more weeks, humiliated and unwelcome. Occasionally, I was joined by the starting punter, who was actually the backup quarterback. He almost never practiced punting. Despite this, his natural athleticism allowed him to kick farther than I could. I have to say, it was disheartening to be no better than the guy who couldn't give a shit.

The season wore on, and as the days grew shorter and cooler, so did my chances of kicking that elusive perfect punt. I couldn't see myself continuing this quest much longer. I wasn't an athlete, and some things we don't get no matter how hard we try. That's what I was thinking one gray, autumn afternoon, as I kneeled on the ground, tying my kicking shoe, almost in prayer.

"You! You're up!" screamed one of the coaches, pointing to me. This time it wasn't to play tight end, but to actually punt during a special-teams drill.

I wanted to decline. It just felt like another opportunity to humiliate myself—a public shaming to prove just how out of touch I was with reality. But how could I say no? What was I doing there, day after day, if not to kick a ball in a game? I jogged onto the field, counting the hash marks so that I was exactly 12 yards behind the center. This was real now, not a meditation, and my pounding heart let me know it. I licked my fingers, because that was part of my routine, or at least my charade, and dried them on the towel tucked neatly under my belt. Then I extended my arms to make a target for the ball. A light rain was starting to fall, which added to my nervousness. The ball would be slick, and my planting foot would be less secure. These were not good conditions to kick in. I felt the eyes of all my teammates beating on me. They were cold and unkind, and I hid from them by reciting the same words that I had used for years to hide from my pain. *Head down, drop it flat, follow through.*

I nodded to the center, and in an instant, the ball came whizzing at my face. It was harder and more violent than it needed to be, and it stung my hands as I caught it.

Head down.

I took two steps forward while quickly rotating the laces into position.

Drop it flat.

I could hear the breath of a grunting player bearing down on me, eager to impress the coach by blocking my kick—denying me the one thing I so desperately wanted, and this enraged me. I swung my leg, urging my thigh to take everything out of me and put it into the ball.

All those hours of punting on adjacent fields ... the teasing from kids ... the teasing from adults ... Everything fell away. This was me in front of my house on a cold-winter's day just after my father had moved out, hiding from my anger and my tears.

Follow through.

Over the years, I had kicked tens of thousands of footballs. Maybe hundreds of thousands. This one felt different. It felt so different, that, for a second, I thought maybe something had gone horribly wrong.

"Head down," I reminded myself. Only when my foot had reached its highest point, way above my head, like that girl on the gymnastics mat, did I finally allow myself to look up. And there it was.

The ball was screaming through the air, higher and higher, its perfect spiral pushing it away from me with such force. I watched it go, and it was beautiful.

I looked downfield at the player who was set to receive the punt. He quickly backpedaled, as the ball was going farther than anyone expected. Realizing that even this wouldn't be enough, he completely turned around and began sprinting to catch up to it, but he couldn't. I had kicked it too far. When the ball finally came back down to the world that I lived in, it was a good 55 yards from the line of scrimmage. Exactly what a pro would kick.

There was a moment of silence. All of us needed to process what had just happened. It didn't add up. Confused, the head coach finally announced, "Who kicked that?"

A hand raised into the air, and I was as surprised as everyone else to discover that it belonged to me.

"Jamin," I said quietly, and the team burst into applause. The same guys who had laughed me out of the huddle were now cheering. A few ripped off their helmets, joyfully high-fiving each other. They were smiling with pride, but in that moment, I'm certain I wasn't. What I felt was relief from deep inside. It was a giant gasp of air after being held underwater for far too long. Whatever had been pulling me down all those years had finally released me from its grip. It was gone now, and I didn't need to kick at it anymore.

A few months later, I was eating in the dining hall. My football jacket was draped over the back of the chair. It was cold outside, and even though my jacket wasn't heavy enough, I wore it anyway. I left it on my chair to re-fill my drink, but when I returned, the jacket was gone. It was stolen or taken by accident. Frantically, I scanned the crowd, and later checked the lost-and-found bin, but I never saw it again. Years of practice, and gone was the only proof that I had ever played college football. Truthfully, it didn't seem right that I had it in the first place, so I stopped looking.

Today, a bag of footballs still hangs in my garage, along with the other half-forgotten relics from my past that I won't let go of. They gather dust and cobwebs, and mostly get in the way. I'm 30 years older now. Thirty years slower and grayer. But every now and then, I drag this bag to an empty field and search for the boy who set me free.

The Ghoul

Sally is an elderly woman, and we exchange pleasantries on days that we haul our trash bins to the curb.

"Good morning, Mike."

"Hi, Sally."

We both wave, so neighborly, from behind the fetid remains of the nastiness we don't want in our homes. It's all very Norman Rockwell–esque if you don't dig much deeper. From far away, I doubt Sally can see me wince when she refers to me as Mike. I've never introduced myself that way, and no one ever calls me that. I'm Michael. I haven't called myself "Mike" since I was a child, because it was easier to spell than "Michael" and impossible to rhyme with "motorcycle." Odder still is how Sally addresses the rest of my family. We discovered this one Christmas when she left a gift on our doorstep. At first, I reacted with dread, thinking that now we had to give her something in return. But then we unwrapped it and realized it was just a tin of pumpkin-spice cocoa that she was clearly re-gifting.

"Why leave cocoa in my garbage," she must've thought, "when I can give it to the neighbors, and they can leave it in theirs." In the end, it wasn't the cocoa that was the gift, it was my subsequent discovery that despite living next to us for 20 years, Sally didn't know any of our names. In the card that she attached, she referred to me as "Mike." Cynthia was "Cindy." Roxy, which is the name on her birth certificate, was "Roxanne," and Lola had the worst name of all. She was simply called "Roxanne's sister." I laughed my ass off when I read that part. I imagined Sally sitting at her kitchen table, scribbling her little Christmas card, then straining to remember Lola's name before finally giving up. "Eh, fuck it. I'll just call her 'Roxanne's sister.'"

This became the Christmas gift that kept on giving, as it provided me with endless opportunities to troll my daughters. At bedtime I'd tuck them in and affectionately say, "I love you, Roxanne," before adding, dismissively, "You too, Roxanne's sister." The joke got old fast, but that didn't stop me from beating it to death when Roxy forgot to bring her dishes to the sink.

"Shame on you, Roxanne. Why can't you be more like Roxanne's sister!"

Despite getting so much enjoyment out of Sally's mishandling of all our names, I was also indignant. How could someone live next door to a person for all these years and never bother to learn their name? It's just wrong. And like a true hypocrite, a few years later, I was guilty of the same exact crime. This came to light when I broke the news to Cynthia that tragedy had struck our neighborhood.

"Did you know that what's-his-face died?" I said, completely in shock.

"Who?"

"The creepy guy two houses down."

"What creepy guy?"

"Undead Fred."

"Undead Fred" is what I'd been calling our neighbor for years, even though the name was only half accurate. The Fred part was not true. His real name might have been Steve or Louis for all I know, but I'm certain he was undead. He had a ghoulishness about him. Tall and bony, he looked like a human whisper—something that would emerge from a fog holding a scythe. It wasn't a black robe that he wore, but rather a dirty tank top that accentuated the concave divot in his chest. I imagine that's where the cannonball hit him two centuries ago. His bushy, dark eyebrows were awnings over his eyes, casting shadows on a face that was as gray as highway cement. Due to how skinny he was, his cheekbones were also sunken, giving his mouth a sort of reverse smile—as if he was only happy to see the far side of his throat. And dangling from his yellow, cadaverous fingers was his constant and only companion—a lit cigarette with a long ash that was afraid to let go because of what might happen next. "Spooky" is how I'd describe Undead Fred, if for some reason I was roped into filling out his Tinder profile.

For the two decades that we lived next to him, Undead Fred never aged. Not one day. He was an eternal 4,000 years old. Whereas we moved into our home in 2001, he'd been living in his run-down shit shack since before man had calendars. None of us in the neighborhood had ever been inside his home, but we all assumed there had to be a well in one of the bedrooms.

"How deep do you suppose it is?"

"Deep enough so that we can't hear the screams."

One night, the stillness of our quiet little street was broken by the arrival of several squad cars. The police swarmed his house as sirens blared and neighbors poured out of their homes. "Go back inside," we were told, and I happily obliged, preferring to be the kind of lookie-loo that peeks at the world from behind closed curtains. The next morning, the rumor on the street was that Undead Fred's teenage son was visiting him, and they got into a heated altercation, culminating with them pulling guns on each other. As shocking as that sounds, all I could think was, "Wait a minute. Someone fucked Undead Fred???"

"Well, 16 years ago," said my neighbor Michelle. She lived across the street. "Can you imagine pointing a gun at your own son?"

"Hold on," I interrupted. "Was it consensual?"

A few days later, when the gun smoke had cleared, Undead Fred retook his familiar station—pacing in his front yard, summoning the apocalypse. The reason why he had time to do this was because he was on disability, although outwardly, he didn't seem to have any physical ailments. The problem, I decided, must've been on the inside—cowering behind the black olives he called eyeballs. And so he passed his days standing on the patch of dirt that once was his front lawn, trying to resurrect the grass with his phantom powers. It was eerie seeing him lurking there, in front of his house, where the windows were never open and the drapes were always shut. What was he hiding? What was he not being honest about?

When Lola was younger, I tried to convince her that Undead Fred was a ghost that only I could see. We drove past him one morning, and my eyes went wide in horror.

"Oh my God!"

"What?"

I pretended to be too terrified to speak. "It's a ... ghost!"

"That's so mean, Dad. Don't even."

"So you see him, too, child! Heavens, I thought I was the only. Be gone, apparition!" I shouted.

"Have you even talked to him?" Lola admonished me. "He might be a nice guy." Lola is much kinder than I am, and she doesn't like it when I make fun of people, which rules out half of everything that comes out of my mouth. I suppose I could've apologized, if for no other reason than to prove that I can be a good person. But getting her to laugh is more important to me, so I really had no choice but to push even further.

"Yeah, you're right. Undead Fred probably has the heart of a child." I added, "In a pickle jar in the basement." And then came the laugh that I so desperately craved.

All that seems less funny now that Undead Fred is Newly Dead Fred. Death has a way of sapping the joy out of so many things. It also makes you reflective. Since his passing, I can't help but to recount our interactions, as brief as they were. Our street hosts a neighborhood block party every few years. At one of them, I recall spotting Undead Fred leaning against a telephone pole, near the barbecue. He was holding a hot dog up to his mouth, and it looked like he was about to bite eternal life into it.

"Come hither," he whispered to the hot dog. "Don't you want to live forever?"

Seeing Undead Fred standing there, awkward and alone, made me feel bad for him. Not bad enough to do anything about it, of course. But throughout the day, I did watch him from the corner of my eye. At one point, I saw him talking with another neighbor. I felt relieved that I wouldn't have to be the one to make him feel welcome. There was just something about Undead Fred that wouldn't allow me to approach. Whatever secrets he was hiding, I didn't want to know. So to put distance between us, I made jokes about him—but only behind his back. I wouldn't have had the courage to do it to his face, so compromises had to be made. I wasn't cruel about it, though. And it's not like he was aware that I made fun of him. I wasn't the popular cheerleader snickering at the nerdy girl, hoping to make her cry. Nothing I said or did was intended to hurt him. And if Undead Fred somehow sensed that, that's on him. Without proof, he was just being paranoid.

Only once did I make small talk with Undead Fred, and that

was because I had no choice. I was walking our dog when she, oblivious to societal decorum, pissed on his lawn. Right in front of his face. The ghoul was only a few feet from his rotting front door, raking leaves over what might have been a freshly dug grave. His gaze slowly raised from the pile, then over toward me, where it grabbed at my neck and began choking me. I tugged at my dog's leash so she could feel it, too.

"You just had to piss on his yard," I muttered under my breath. Undead Fred stared at me, but it was impossible to tell if he was angry or aroused. His look was blank, encouraging me to feel whatever emotion was most handy. Terror was the first thing I pulled out of my pocket.

"Sorry about that," I said awkwardly as Undead Fred scraped the metal teeth of his rake against the sunbaked dirt. He paused, his lips pursing as his mind formulated what to say. I braced for what would come from his mouth. Maybe a swarm of bees. Finally, from deep within his stomach, he growled, "That's a golden retriever."

His gravelly words cascaded from his mouth, forming puddles of rock at his feet. I stared at them for too long before finally responding, "Yes, it is!" I said it with enthusiasm, pretending to be impressed by the fact that he correctly identified the most common breed in the world. He could've just as easily said, "That's a dog."

"Why, yes, it is a dog! You sure know your animals, Undead Fred!"

And so I just stood there, smiling uncomfortably while my golden retriever decided how much piss to unload, starting and stopping as if she were adding salt to a recipe. "Seasoning to taste" is how I would describe it. To the best of my memory, that's all we said that day, me and Undead Fred. In the years that passed, I sometimes waved to him from behind the safety of my locked car, but that was all I could offer. When I heard the news of his passing, I didn't know how to take it. I was supposed to be sad, right?

His house stood vacant for a long time. If his son came to collect any personal belongings, I never saw him. What I did see was a house that really looked no different than when Undead Fred was alive. The curtains on the windows were still drawn shut, and the weeds growing in his front yard were as tall as ever. It was like he was still there—haunting the place. Then one morning a cleaning crew arrived. They wore masks to protect themselves from breathing the air in his home. Toiling under the hot sun, they threw the contents of Newly Dead Fred's life into heaps on the front yard. Towering over a small pile marked DONATION was a mountain marked GARBAGE. That's when things became obvious—Undead Fred was a hoarder, living in a prison of his own making. At that moment, I became truly saddened by his passing. Not by the tragedy of his death, but by the tragedy of his life.

When the cleaning crew had finally left the job site to have their skin scrubbed with a wire brush, I watched as a real-estate agent pounded a FOR SALE sign into the hardened ground of the front yard. It was violent, the way she hit it, and it made me think of a vampire being driven with a stake. Undead Fred would've loved it.

"Do you think the real-estate agent would let me go inside just to take some photos?" my daughter Roxy asked me. She was home for a few weeks before art school started again.

"Probably not, but why would you even want to?"

"I just think it would be so interesting."

"With the hantavirus and the cooties ... you don't want to go in there."

Her face fell in disappointment, almost embarrassed for having asked my opinion. I could feel her pull away when I said it, and I knew I'd made a mistake. Roxy has always been interested in stuff that others might find strange. Like alchemy. She reads esoteric books and quotes little-known experts on a subject that, for the most part, has been irrelevant for centuries. But the idea that she might want to tour the home of a deceased hoarder ... that just seemed too much ... so I corrected her. I told her she didn't want to go inside, even though she told me the exact opposite.

The following morning, as I was returning home from a run, I stopped by my neighbor Michelle's house to say hello. She was in her garage with the door open, working at her potter's wheel. She and her daughter had both graduated from art school, so Roxy liked to spend time with them. They all saw the world the way artists do—finding beauty in unlikely places. A glob of salsa could spill on the floor, and one of them would take a picture because of the way the tomato chunks stood majestic against the carpeting.

"Hey, do you want to check out the inside of that creepy house?" Michelle asked.

"No. And why does everyone want to go in there?"

"Aren't you a little curious?"

"Not really, but I'll go with you if you want." I said this mostly because I wanted to correct myself from how I responded to Roxy.

To be honest, I was curious. But invading the ghoul's private life now that he was dead struck me as unfair, especially since I showed no interest when he was alive. Plus, given how I felt about him, I didn't know if I could look at his home without being judgmental. That's a quality I loathe in myself, even though I'm so damn good at it you'd think I'd be proud.

Michelle and I walked up to his house, each footstep bringing us closer than we'd ever been before. As we neared, the chipping paint became more obvious, as did the dry rot and termite damage. It was a house devouring itself, and as the details came into focus, so did Undead Fred—so troubled and tortured. We stared at the house in silence, observing the sanctity of the moment. Eager to ease the tension, I put my arm around Michelle and blurted, "Oh, honey, it's perfect!" pretending to be a young couple buying a starter home. "And once we clear out the skeletons, we can turn the garage into your studio!"

"The schools here are supposed to be great!" she said, playing along.

Attached to the front door was a digital lockbox installed by the real-estate agent. Its newness looked grossly out of place. Because of it, there was no way to get through the door, but there was a large window in the living room that was cracked open. It probably hadn't shut properly for decades, causing water to drain into the house whenever it rained. It was easy enough to slide the window farther open so that we could pass through.

"Top-notch schools. Top notch!" I said while climbing through the window. "Although the neighbors are a little nosy."

Once inside, my eyes adjusted to the darkness of it all, as did my conscience. The house had been stripped bare by the cleaning crew, but the stains and enduring smell made it easy to imagine how it once was: every room and hallway jam-packed with foul and acrid garbage. The filth had permeated the fibers of the curtains, the glaze on the kitchen tiles, and the metal faucets of the bathroom. The plaster walls were covered in a brownish-yellow film that was tacky to the touch. This undoubtedly was caused by all the cigarettes that Undead Fred had smoked, sucking life from them like it was a virgin's neck. By the front door, the wood lath beneath the plaster was completely exposed, as if Undead Fred, trapped like a rat in his own home, angrily tried to gnaw his way out. The hardwood floors beneath our feet were squishy, making me fear they'd give way. Then I realized that the floor was actually carpeting that was so worn, matted, and dirty, I mistook it for rotting wood.

"Jesus," I gasped, pulling my shirt over my mouth, careful not to inhale anything. We headed to the kitchen, where the countertop was covered in so much rat shit, rust, and cigarette ash, it was now part of the surface. The bottom of the counter barely touched the floor because someone had violently kicked it away. The pipes to the kitchen faucet, which should've been hidden inside the wall, were completely exposed. At one point, there must have been a leak in the wall, so Undead Fred must've torn it open. But he never bothered to restore the tiles. There was just a big, gaping wound, and the symbolism wasn't lost on me.

In the house's sole bathroom, the sink held a brown puddle, which made it look like the last watering hole in the Serengeti, where animals both drank out of and shat into. This is where he brushed his teeth? But the feature that stood out most was the bathtub. It was encased in a layer of blackened grime, reminding me of an old oven tray, caked with burned food. Standing in the tub would've only made you dirtier, which made me realize that Undead Fred never bathed. Although the cleaning crew emptied the house of almost everything, the one thing they couldn't remove was his pain. And it was everywhere. This is where Undead Fred dwelled, captive to things he couldn't let go of. Everything—every scrap of garbage and speck of dirt—must've seemed dear to him.

My tour lasted only a few minutes. This was no place to hang around. I took one final look around and climbed out the front window, then I gasped for air. I tried to process the horror of what I'd just seen, but where do you begin with something like that? What's the starting point, when everything just gets worse and worse? Moments later, Michelle climbed out the window, too. I half expected her to vomit on the curb, but instead she had a big smile on her face.

"Roxy should go inside. She'd love this!"

Of all the things I witnessed that morning—the dirt-ringed tub, the filthy counters that he rested his food on, the walls that bled nicotine—hearing Michelle say those words was perhaps the most shocking. How did she know that Roxy would love it, when only a few days earlier it took me by surprise? She understood my own daughter better than I did, and it hit me like a cannonball to the chest.

There's so much about Roxy—this beautiful, perfect baby that I took home from the hospital—that I no longer know. We used to be so close. Best friends, really. Although that's not how I introduced her to people when she was little.

"This is my daughter ... " I used to say, full of pride. Then I'd pause while looking at her. "I'm so sorry, I'm completely drawing a blank on your name."

"It's Roxy!" she'd shout.

"Yes, of course. Roxy," I'd respond, with relief. Then I'd tentatively continue, "Is that 'Roxy' with an *ie* or 'Roxy' with a *y*?"

"*Y!*"

"I'm just curious, that's all. You don't have to get mad about it." Then she'd laugh with frustration.

Watching a four-year-old grow exasperated with her father's stupidity is hilarious. It really is so much fun. As they get older, it's less so.

When she was in middle school, we developed a magic act together. This was for a show we were going to perform for her class. We spent weeks holed up in her bedroom, rehearsing. It was a mind-reading act that was so convincing, you would've thought Roxy was an actual psychic. The day of the performance, I stood at the head of the class and introduced her as having an amazing ability that confounded us all. "We discovered it when she was a baby, and despite traveling the country, consulting specialist after specialist to find the cause of her superpower, we could never get an adequate answer. So it's just something that we live with now, keeping one step ahead of the scientists who wish to dissect and study her."

As a demonstration, I asked one of her classmates to choose a card from the deck and show it to everyone except for Roxy. She was standing in the corner, her back turned to the crowd. The student could have chosen any card out of 52, but in this case, it was the six of diamonds.

"Now, Roxy," I called off. "I want you to fix an image in your head."

That's all I said, and the room fell silent. She concentrated, struggling to pull the image of the card out of thin air. Then, exhausted, she finally announced, "Your card is the six of diamonds." Jaws hit the floor. It was a miracle—a father-daughter act you couldn't believe.

What no one realized was that when I said, "Now fix an image in your head," "now" was our code word for diamonds, and "fix" meant six. We had a code for every card in the deck, and we replicated this trick over and over, proving how special she was. Of course, only Roxy and I knew the truth. It was our secret. I was so proud, that day. Not because of our little magic trick, but because of how we were together. We were magic.

But somewhere along the course of our relationship, I fucked up. Not in a big way, but in a series of little ways. They were tiny —small enough to go almost unnoticed. It began when Roxy grew into a teenager and committed the crime of turning into someone who I had problems with—me. We started fighting. And because we're so similar, she insisted she knew me, and I insisted I knew her, and we argued over it. This was our thing, and

I just assumed that we'd always be connected this way, interlocked in battle for the rest of our lives, but still interlocked. But that stopped being the case when she moved away for college. She packed up as much as she could carry and left, leaving me with something even heavier. Regret. I missed her so, and I wondered why I ever fought with her in the first place.

Now when she returns home, she seems different. There's more new and less old. I can be completely in her presence, sitting together at the dinner table, and yet still feel so far away. When she's not home, I send her texts every few days. "I love you." "I'm proud of you." "You're doing great." They're like messages in a bottle, and most of them don't get answered. But still I send them, hoping that one day she'll find them all.

I tell myself a lie to make this go down easier: that she's starting her own journey. That there are supposed to be new chapters of her life, entire parts of herself, that only other people get to know. And it's all because I did such a good job raising her. This lie, disguised as a compliment, makes the distance between me and my daughter feel natural and not my fault. It's such a good lie.

* * *

On a late-summer morning, we loaded the car with Roxy's luggage. College was starting again, and Cynthia was taking her to the airport. I would've gone, but they were stopping to pick up Roxy's boyfriend on the way.

"You know how it is," says Cynthia, telling me a different lie.

I smile, pretending that it's privacy that Roxy wants. Or that the car is too small to fit me. Or any number of other stories that can easily do the trick.

I hug my daughter tight, kissing her cheeks more than she

cares for—holding her for longer than she wants. I used to do the same when she was little, her long, curly hair brushing against my eyes. This is back when I did everything right.

"Take good care of my baby," I whisper into her ear, as if she were mine and not her own. I squeeze her tightly because I want her to feel my love. But really feel it, deep inside. Embraced. She smiles politely.

From our driveway I watch as my perfect little girl closes the car door. The lie is over now. Now begins the truth. The parts of herself that she doesn't share with me ... those are things she doesn't *want* to share with me. Secrets that I can't be trusted with, or, at the very least, didn't earn. I don't blame her. There were so many times when I second-guessed her decisions or just didn't help her be who she was. I can play them back in my head, and see them all so clearly. I thought I was raising her. But instead of feeling my love, she felt my judgment. It's a quality that she often saw in me, and now that judgment is deep inside her. If I held up a playing card today, would she still read my mind? Would she even care to try? The engine revs, and then she pulls away.

I'm alone now, and the sun burns even hotter. It pounds me into the hardened dirt, anchoring my feet in place. I can feel my breathing turn heavy and labored, as if my once contented soul has just given up on me in disgust. I remain here long after my daughter is gone, incapacitated with grief, unable to let go. How I must appear to cars passing by, so vacant yet so full of shame. Like a ghoul haunting his yard, I imagine.

Rapid Italian

A few years ago, I realized I had completely run out of new things to say. Everything I said was just a repeat of something I had said a million times before. "Is the front door locked?" "I can't believe how hot it is outside." "Are your hands as dry as mine?" It was as if I was trying to remind myself of how boring I had become. And I wasn't just tired of hearing myself, I was also tired of being myself. But how do you become someone else without doing something drastic, like faking your own death or using Axe Body Spray? So instead, I just grew quiet, retreating into my brain. That's where I go when I'm sad or anxious. Here, but not present. At first, I don't think many people noticed my absence, or, if they did, they were grateful for the reprieve. But after a while, Cynthia began to worry.

"What's going on in there?" she said, touching my head. "It's like you've disappeared into your little turtle shell."

That was the perfect way to describe it, and it was no coincidence. As a child, I kept a turtle in a tank in my bedroom. Her name was Myrtle, although she may have been a male. When I think back on Myrtle the Turtle, I wonder why I didn't spend more time trying to determine her gender. The name I gave her wasn't particularly clever, but it rhymed, and when you're a child, that passes for funny. No matter, really. I didn't like her or him much anyway. I was more attracted to the *idea* of Myrtle. With the shell on her back, she was always safe at home. When things got scary or uncomfortable, she could tuck her arms and legs inside, leaving only her scaly elbows exposed. She wasn't a fighter, and she wasn't a runner. She was a fortress. Deep inside herself she'd hide until the threat eventually grew bored and went away. To me, that seemed like perfect compromise between a hero and a coward: a Howard. Maybe that would've been a better name.

Of course, keeping a salmonella-ridden reptile in my bedroom had its drawbacks. Setting aside catching dysentery, a turtle is an impossibly boring pet. Only rarely would she move off the flat piece of shale I used to decorate her tank, and even then it was usually in the middle of the night with a startling thunk.

"You okay, Myrtle?" I'd whisper, and she'd ignore me in her passive-aggressive turtle-y way. She must've absolutely hated living in my bedroom. Despite her silence, I could never fully forget Myrtle's presence. Myrtle had a habit of casually flinging her own waste against the glass walls of her tank. Prisoners do this when they've lost all hope. Cleaning her aquarium was too much of a bother, so instead I just let everything roast beneath the heat lamp, until it was sewage cooked *al dente.*

One day, I came to the profound realization that Myrtle didn't deserve to be caged. She was a wild animal that was born free and should live that way. I decided I would take her to a nearby pond, let her go, and allow her to enjoy the rest of her life. Then I came to an even deeper realization: what Myrtle needed even more than freedom ... was a friend. Someone she could share her existence with, as miserable as it was. Yes, that would be even kinder of me! On a trip upstate, I found the perfect companion. It was a toad that I quickly named Fried Chicken because of the bubbly texture of his skin. After catching him with my baseball cap, I staged a bogus trial on a trumped-up charge, and sentenced him to a life without nature. He looked sallow and tired when we finally returned home and I dropped him inside Myrtle's tank. But that was to be expected for an amphibian who'd been unjustly sentenced. Once the initial shock wore off that he'd never enjoy the feeling of cold spring water against his face, he'd be as happy as ever.

Feeding a turtle and a toad was another matter. The books suggested flies, crickets, worms, and maggots, but that was a bridge too far for my mother. Maybe she worried I'd try to keep them as pets, too. Instead, she decided that I should feed them pre-packaged shrimp cocktails from the supermarket. Easy to prepare, yet fancy enough for black-tie occasions. I dumped a glassful into their tank, landing with a lifeless plop. Whatever Myrtle didn't eat, Fried Chicken would shit on, and Myrtle would eat later. The combined stench quickly permeated the fibers in my clothing and the curls in my hair, and soon it was near impossible to sit next to me at the dinner table without retching.

"It's Mom's raisin baked ziti," I told my sister. But that was a lie. Mom's raisin baked ziti smelled perfectly fine. It only looked, tasted, and sounded bad.

Eventually, I was told to eat meals in my bedroom, where I became as isolated from the world as Myrtle and Fried Chicken. In what can only be described as poetic justice, it was I that became imprisoned. "Let us out!" we all shouted. "Let us out!"

Within a few days, Fried Chicken was dead, having succumbed to the toxic fumes of Myrtle's tank. I warned him to stay low, beneath the poisonous cloud, but toads being toads love to hop.

"You learned the hard way," I said, as I tossed his lifeless body into the trash can beside my nightstand. I can't say I was too broken up about it. By nightfall I had forgotten all about Fried Chicken, even as his decaying corpse added to the fetid gases hovering by my pillow.

One hot summer morning, when the air in my bedroom was particularly ripe with rotting crustacean and reptile refuse, my father decided Myrtle could use some fresh air. Something to remind her of the good ol' days, before her human overlord introduced misery to the Garden of Eden. He carried her tank outside and set it beneath a tree.

"Don't worry," he told me. "She'll be fine in the shade."

Tragically, my father wasn't aware that planet Earth rotates on its axis. In a few hours, the sun made its way across the sky, and the shade no longer fell on Myrtle's tank, completely exposing her to the scorching heat of its unrelenting rays. By early evening, Myrtle was dead ... baked inside her own shell.

"Funny how things work out for the best," confided my father to my mother. If he felt guilty about it, he hid it well. I can only imagine that the two of them were so happy they wanted to dance on the roof. The only remaining issue was how to break the news to their delicate son. There's a good chance that if they simply returned the tank to my bedroom, dead Myrtle and all, I wouldn't have noticed for a few months. But that would've been duplicitous. Involuntary turtle slaughter was one thing, but conspiracy to hide the crime was another. They decided to be honest with me, mostly because it aligned with keeping the smell of roasted turtle far from their own bedroom.

When my father told me of Myrtle's death, I sobbed furiously, screaming at the horror of it all. Steam was still coming out of her nostrils. Truthfully, mine were crocodile tears—a fitting tribute to my fallen reptilian friend. With her stinky-stanky tanky no longer poisoning my room, I could finally feel air in my lungs again. And that, years later as an adult, is what I aspired to be when I grew tired of hearing my own words. A turtle.

"You're not a turtle!" Cynthia yelled at me. "You can't be in a world full of people and not talk."

I tried to explain that I wasn't sending a message to anyone. I just didn't know how to participate without completely boring myself. I don't have a philosophy worth sharing, or a cure that I'm holding back. Just a headful of words, rattling around like ping-pong balls in a lottery machine. It's possible that Cynthia had more to say on this matter, but I didn't hear it. I was already deep inside my shell.

At the time, I was writing on a sitcom with a work environment more toxic than my childhood bedroom. That's not uncommon in Hollywood. Writers are hired to be creative, and forgiven when they're assholes. The staff consisted mainly of 23-year-olds with no professional-writing experience, which might seem odd given the job requirements. The showrunner was only a few years older than me, but he confided that he wanted writers fresh out of college because their dialogue sounded hip and relevant. "Not like us old guys," he said, nudging me. I was 38.

But the young writers didn't know how to pitch anything usable, unless you consider adding the phrase "and shit" to the end of every line of dialogue as a contribution to the literary canon. So if someone had a character say, "Let's go out for tacos," they would change that to, "Let's go out for tacos and shit." The boss was enamored by their youthful irreverence, and encouraged them to tear apart everyone else's script to work their millennial magic. Eventually, the older writers on the show grew dead inside.

The hour-and-a-half commute to this job felt cruelly short in the morning, and unbearably long in the evening. I decided that my time sitting in traffic should be spent on something more productive than just shaking my head in disbelief, so I searched online and discovered a few courses that taught Italian in your car. Who wouldn't want to speak Italian, when everything sounds like a love letter. "*Sei cosi brutta anche la morte ha paura di te.*" That means you're so ugly, even death is scared of you. But come on, if someone said that to you, you'd melt in their arms. I was convinced I needed to learn Italian, but what pushed me over the top was the tagline for one of the courses. "When you learn a new language, you gain a new soul."

A new soul. It sounded so tempting. With a new soul, I could be more than just content, I could be ebullient. My old soul never would've said "ebullient." Within seconds I was paying for expedited shipping.

I wound up buying a British course called Rapid Italian because all the lessons were set to catchy music, which was supposed to make it easier to learn. "*Cerotti*, *cerotti*, doo-ahhh, *cerotti*." Over and over I repeated "*cerotti*," until it flowed effortlessly out of my mouth, and I didn't even know what it meant yet. Finally, the speaker revealed the translation: "plasters."

"Plasters?" I yelled. "What the fuck is a plaster?!" Was it a type of drywall? Now American English wasn't enough—I had to learn how to speak English English as well?

I later discovered that plasters were what Brits called bandages. But what does a bandage have to do with plaster? I was mad at the British for using a word that made absolutely no sense, then forgave them when it occurred to me that our word, "Band-Aid," was equally dumb.

For months, repeating Italian words aloud during my commute became routine, and I enjoyed new and unfamiliar sounds rolling off my tongue. My days at work may have been dreadful, but at least I could pretend to be someone else during the drive. And when the hip millennials held the writers' room hostage with their young-speak, I could disappear inside my turtle shell, reciting the most recent phrases I had learned.

One day, while walking from the parking lot to the office, one of the young writers caught up to me.

"I saw you singing in your car," he said, mocking me.

"I wasn't singing. I'm learning Italian."

"Oh, yeah? Going to Italy? Does the boss know?"

"I'm not going to Italy."

We waited in silence for the elevator to arrive, and I recalled Cynthia's warning that when I don't speak, people think I hate them. I did hate this guy, so my messaging was on point.

"Do you come from an Italian family and shit?"

"New York Jews," I responded.

He nodded, pretending to be satisfied, but I knew this was driving him crazy, and I enjoyed being a jerk to him. We stepped into the elevator, and I watched the numbers above the door as we ascended, wondering how many would have to light up before he asked his next question. Only two.

"So when do you plan on speaking it?"

"I don't know."

This was just about too much for his young head to take, and he laughed derisively.

"Then why are you learning Italian in your car?"

I waited for the doors to open, and when they did, I stepped out first, leaving him behind.

"Because I've said everything I wanted to say in English."

A few months passed, and I was ready to replace my beginner-level CDs with intermediate lessons offered by other companies. The jazzy nightclub music may have lured me off the street, but if I really wanted to learn something, I had to go into the back room, which was reserved for serious students. There, the "doo-ahhh"s were replaced by the mind-numbing repetition of a lecturer walking through various conjugation charts. This guy sounded half asleep—like he'd just downed a bottle of NyQuil on his way back from an audit. But repetition is the key to learning a language, and there's no way around it. New words have to be brutally beaten into your head, over and over, until that one moment ... that sublime touch from God ... when your brain has become so pulverized that it's finally able to speak a foreign language without thinking. It took months of daily practice to get there, but when I did, it was like flicking on the field lights at an outdoor stadium. Darkness became light. I didn't need to conjugate words into Italian, I could just talk, and that transformation amazed me. "Who is this person? I don't speak Italian."

By June, I was ready to graduate to more difficult lessons, but I couldn't find any advanced Italian CDs on the Internet. So instead I bought a college textbook, read it into my iPhone, and played it back in the car. It was during one of these lessons that I was pulled over by a cop. The police officer saw me talking in my car, and accused me of being distracted by my cellphone. I told him that wasn't the case. I was learning Italian, then I played a bit of my recording.

"*Lo avrei comprato se avessi avuto i soldi.* I would have bought it if I had the money. Past-conditional tense combined with past subjunctive," I explained. "That's some high-level stuff." I was hoping I could be forgiven for missing a street sign when I was concentrating on something as complex as that. But apparently I couldn't be, and he wrote the ticket anyway.

"*Vaffanculo,*" I muttered.

The ticket was bullshit. I wasn't speeding. I just took a right-hand turn out of Trader Joe's onto a quiet street. The NO RIGHT TURN sign had been put up by the locals because they didn't want people driving in their neighborhood. Well, too bad. Don't live on a road, then. And the cops liked enforcing it because it was easy revenue for the city. This is what the cops ticketed me for—a cautious right-hand turn down a quiet street. Every morning, my neighborhood roars with white BMWs doing 90 in a school zone. They're teenage boys driving their parents' cars. Roll down their windows and a cloud of Paco Rabanne spills out like vape smoke. Pull *them* over!

By the time I arrived home, I had decided that despite being 100 percent guilty, I was 100 percent innocent. I would fight the ticket. Maybe I was still under the influence of all the Italian grammar I'd been parroting. Italians don't take any shit. Of course I didn't have any evidence to support my case, but I had something even more powerful—righteous indignation. That's a trick I learned from my mother. When I was 10, she crashed into a police car, and it was completely her fault. But the minute she stepped out of the car, she started screaming at the cops. Just completely unloading.

"What the fuck were you thinking?! Were you even thinking at all?!"

The police were as shocked as the rest of us. I mean, who yells at an officer of the law like that? But instead of putting her in handcuffs, they apologized profusely, promised the city would pay for the repairs, and we returned home having just witnessed a magic trick.

I was hoping that my similar outrage would be enough to convince a judge to toss my case. Just yell. I once had a therapist who said that my inflated sense of justice wasn't making me a happier person. Well, this would show him!

My court appointment was for one P.M., but I showed up 30 minutes early as a compromise to my anxiety, which had been lobbying for me to camp out the night before. When I arrived, I was disappointed to discover that the courthouse looked like a Soviet-era project used to warehouse dissidents. It lacked the grandeur that should be afforded matters concerning the law, and I questioned my decision to dress up, when clearly the building hadn't bothered.

The courtroom doors were locked, and taped to them was a schedule of appearances. Even though I received a confirmation notice for one P.M., the makeshift sign said that court wouldn't resume until 1:30.

"Oh, no," I thought. "How can I win when they can change the rules?"

Looking for a place to sit, I retreated to the cinder-block breezeway filled with other defendants. It reminded me of a certain depressing tank I kept in my childhood bedroom, only instead of a shale, the benches were made of concrete. I gave one final look around, put on my sunglasses, then retreated deep into the safety of my turtle shell. I would've been happy enough to remain there, but something from the outside world caught my attention. It was an elderly couple reading the schedule on the locked door. They both looked confused, and surprisingly, were speaking in Italian. For the moment, I decided to keep to myself. Interacting with strangers is out of my comfort zone, so I glanced around to see if maybe a Good Samaritan might step up, as if speaking Italian were the same as lending someone jumper cables. Finally, because no one else would say anything, I poked my head out and interrupted.

"*Non è ancora aperto. Aspettiamo qua.*" ("It's not open yet, so we're waiting here.")

Immediately, she looked relieved. So did I. That wasn't as hard as I thought it would be.

"*Ah bene,*" she replied. "*Pensavo che si aprisse all'una.*" ("Oh, good. I thought it opened at one.")

"*Anch'io,*" I reassured her, and I returned to reading my phone. Then she and her husband sat down right next to me, confirming my deepest fear. I was the guy who gives a stray dog some food, and now he's got a puppy following him home. I tried to run away, but she pulled out her cell phone and opened her photos.

"*Ho girato a la sinestra,* and they hit me with a ticket," she said in Italian, showing me a picture of the intersection where she was fined. She swiped to the right to show me a few more angles, and then finally a photo of a woman.

"*E questa mia figlia,*" she said. "My daughter. And she just had a baby."

What was I supposed to do now? She had just confessed to a crime, then brought me home to meet her family. I had no choice but to pull out my cell phone and do the same.

"*Il parcheggio di Trader Joe's, vede il segno* NO RIGHT TURN. *E questa donna è mia moglie,*" I said in Italian, showing her a photo of Cynthia.

"*Bellissima,*" she replied. I smiled politely, then put my phone away, satisfied that nothing else had to be said or done. Everything was now square. I had fulfilled my obligation as a good-ish human being. A moment passed, and then as if compelled by something higher, I pulled out my phone and started swiping again.

"This is my daughter Roxy, *lei sta studiando l'arte.* Here's my other daughter, Lola, *è più giovane, peró* she'll find herself. This is my dog who died *qualche anno fa. Ho pianto tantissimo. Mi manca.* And here's a photo of a light bulb that blew out. I need to buy a matching one, and it's gonna be tricky, *ma c'è la faccio.*"

"Giovanna," she said, offering her hand.

"Michele." I gave her the Italian version of my name, which is who I was at that moment.

As we waited for the slow gears of justice to grind us into polenta, Giovanna and I chatted about all things trivial, connecting the way two people are supposed to, and soon she was sharing details of her life's story. She met her second husband a few years ago in Paris, and was surprised to have found love again so late in life. He was born in Morocco but moved around to other countries, so he spoke five languages, but now he was practically deaf.

"*Mi dispiace,*" I said.

Giovanna told me that the last few years of her career were spent teaching Italian to children at a local immersion elementary school, the same school that a friend of mine sent his daughter to.

"*Non me lo dire,*" I said. "Just one degree of separation."

We chatted for hours like this. *Quattro chiacchiere,* they call it in Italian. At times I struggled with the grammar, trying to recall the correct conjugation of an irregular verb. But she was patient with me, because she appreciated my effort.

Later that day, I was standing before the judge, presenting the true version of my moving violation ... which, sadly, was exactly how the police officer described it. Everyone knew I was guilty. Even Giovanna was looking at me sideways. But I did go through the trouble of appearing before the court, and I pointed that out to the judge.

"Taking time off from work, finding parking, the horrible benches you make us sit on ... Yes, I'm guilty, but shouldn't that make me innocent?"

The judge wasn't about to let me off the hook, but he offered me a third choice. If I took it, he'd cut my fine in half. All I had to do was plead "no contest." I didn't know what that meant, so I asked him to explain it. "No contest" was about accepting conviction without admitting guilt. Truthfully, it sounded like judicial horseshit, and I quickly took the deal.

"I plead 'no contest,' Your Honor," accepting my reward for making an effort.

At the cashier's station, where I went to pay my fine, I passed my credit card beneath the thick, Lucite barrier that protected the clerk from the world. She seemed so at ease behind her transparent wall. We were only two feet apart, yet I had to lean into the crack just to get a sense of her words.

"We don't accept American Express," she mouthed. For a moment I was annoyed. That's my business credit card, and now I couldn't write this experience off as an illegitimate expense. Giovanna and her husband were standing close behind when she heard me complain.

"*Dovresti pensarci come un regalino al governo,*" she said, touching my shoulder. ("You should think of it as a little gift to the government.") Maybe she was right. A thank-you gift.

I said goodbye to Giovanna, surprised that I had enjoyed spending an afternoon with someone I'd likely never see again. Unless, of course, we slammed into each other in the parking lot, which seemed entirely possible. But did I really spend the afternoon with Giovanna? Michael barely said a word. He was hiding. Protecting himself. Michele did all the talking. He was the fun one connecting with a stranger and sharing a few laughs, not me. I just can't do it on my own. It's not who I am.

The halls were crowded now, with more defendants nervously waiting for their day in court. Would they be innocent or guilty?

"There's a third choice," I considered telling them. "You can plead 'no contest.'" But that seemed like something Michele would say, not me, so I kept to myself and headed toward the door. As I was leaving, I noticed my reflection in a window, and slowed down just long enough to see an unfamiliar smile on my face.

"Who is that guy?" I wondered. "Is that the new soul I was promised? And if so, when would I see him again, and what would I do if I did?"

The House on Witherspoon Street

My creative writing professor carried two bags to class. One was an old leather satchel that was well worn and etched with character. It had a large, cumbersome buckle that transformed the simple act of opening a bag into a ribbon-cutting ceremony for a car wash. We'd watch expectantly as he labored to release the metal prong from its hole, then slowly pull the perforated strap from under the bar. Then finally, triumphantly, he'd extract a copy of whichever literary giant we were going to study that day, maybe Tobias Wolff or Shirley Jackson. Simply put, this was the bag we all aspired to have our work pulled out of one day. The stories we wrote, however, were kept in a separate bag. This one was brown, made of paper, and he received it free from the supermarket with his purchase of tuna salad.

As part of the curriculum, the students would often exchange their homework assignments for critique. Some of the kids were wary about putting their short stories in the hands of others. It's not that they couldn't take criticism. They were worried that someone might steal their idea and make it their own. I didn't have that same fear, and it's not because I was brave. It's because I was honest with myself.

"I was hoping to talk to you a little more about my piece," I said to my professor one day after class. I wanted to make sure that my assignment showed improvement over my earlier work. He had scribbled notes in the margin, but they were deliberately vague. "Wow!" with an exclamation point could either mean "Wow, this is good" or "Wow, I can't believe you thought this was good." Now, cornered by me and forced to elaborate, he lit a cigarette and crammed it between his lips.

"It's good," he said. His voice went up an octave on "good." It's *good!* Voices don't pitch like that when they're telling the truth.

I knew the other professors didn't like my writing, which is why I wasn't allowed to major in the creative writing program. My problem was this: Good writing requires two things. You need to have something to say, and you need to know how to say it. I had neither—just a deep desire to be heard. But that's why I wanted to study creative writing—so that someone could teach me how to express the feelings inside me and say them without saying them.

The first time I was rejected from the program, I told myself not to worry. I'd improve and get accepted next year. That didn't happen, though, and strike two was really hard to take. I dreamed of being a TV writer, and it felt like the school wasn't just ruling out my future, it was advising me to not even dream. That's a cold splash of water for a 19-year-old. It was my roommate's idea to try my hand at something a step easier. Copywriting. He screamed this into my ear while I was giving him a ride to our film-studies class on the back of my bike. This is how we often got around campus, me and Ryan. He sat on the seat with his hands on my shoulders while I stood on the pedals.

"There's a radio station on Witherspoon Street. Maybe you can get an internship there!" he shouted.

"What?"

"There's a radio station on Witherspoon!"

"What?"

I couldn't hear Ryan over the squeaking of the wheels, which screamed with every rotation like they were being murdered. My bike was an old ten-speed with wheels that were so bent out of shape you had to pedal just to roll downhill. It was an anti-gravity bike. Despite being a piece of crap, it was my piece of crap, so I always secured it to the bike racks with an expensive U-shaped lock. It must've cost $70, which was way more than the bike was worth. I used to say that I had the bike so that people wouldn't steal my lock. Once, when I was in a hurry to retrieve a book from the library, I left my bicycle outside without locking it. When I returned, my bike was gone. For a moment, I felt angry and violated. But then I found it, 50 yards away, lying in the middle of the courtyard. The thief must've tried to ride away, then ditched it, realizing that some things just weren't worth stealing. That's how I felt about exchanging my creative writing pieces with the other students. Who'd want to take them?

I liked Ryan's idea of working in radio. Having my words broadcast over the airwaves, as opposed to written on the page, seemed glamorous. Not quite Hollywood, but almost Hollywood. I typed a query letter to the station manager, deliberating over every word to prove that I was worthy of such an honor. A week later, my heart jumped when he called to grant me an audience.

According to the map, the trek from my dorm room to the radio station would take about 15 minutes. I didn't know what the station looked like, but in my mind, it had to be spectacular. This is the power of radio. Lacking the visuals of television, it allows us to imagine. For a building to be worthy of housing all these hit songs by famous musicians, it would have to be postmodern with large glass windows and exposed steel girders. There would be a receptionist sitting in a lobby that would be as white as the gates to Heaven. Behind her would be some kind of water feature. Not the kind that sounds like a toilet flushing, but the peaceful kind that sounds like a toilet leaking water from the tank above. I was looking for a building like this, which is why I walked right past the station, completely missing it. I only realized it three blocks later, and I quickly doubled back.

"This can't be right," I said to myself when I finally found the address on the door. My heart sunk into my shoes. This was just a small, postwar tract house with the station call letters posted on the door. How could something as important as a radio station have a rusting basketball hoop over the garage?

The front door was cracked open, and I called out, "Hi, I'm here to see the station manager." I said it tentatively, so as not to tear the fabric of the universe. A voice from down the hall replied, "Be right with you." That, fortunately, turned out to be the receptionist, but it could've just as easily been an elderly woman expecting her Meals on Wheels delivery.

I entered the station, which looked exactly like an ordinary home, other than the thin, industrial-grade carpeting that covered the entryway. There were still pegs by the front door where the previous family hung their coats. Upstairs, in what must've been a bedroom at some point, was the recording studio. It wasn't even in the main bedroom, but rather in a kid's bedroom. The youngest one's, probably. The one who got stuck with the shitty stuff. An ON AIR sign hung over the door, but at one point, it could've just as easily been a sign that read, NO GIRLS ALLOWED, with a backward letter *R*. Plastered nearby were industry awards. They weren't Grammys, although they were designed to look like them. They were just self-congratulatory plaques from various trade organizations. They seemed rescued, suggesting that if they weren't hanging on the wall they'd be at the recycling center, sliding down a conveyor belt on their way to becoming something more prestigious ... like an aluminum can. Radio had always struck me as magical, and now that I was behind the scenes, I saw how the trick was done, and it made me feel stupid for having been fooled.

The receptionist pointed me in the direction of another bedroom down the hall, and when I approached it, an overweight, balding man sitting behind a wooden desk waved me in. His back was to a dormer, where the remnants of a Tot Finder sticker were glued to the window. This turned out to be the man with the highest position there, the station manager, but he couldn't have looked less dignified if he were sitting on a toilet. He wore thick suspenders, making it seem as if he had a parachute strapped to his back. Any moment he might realize the futility of this place, dive out the window, and drift to safety. I sat down in the chair opposite him.

"So you want to be in radio?" he said.

I nodded, but in reality I wasn't sure if I even wanted to *listen* to radio anymore. My eyes landed on the window bench where a laundry hamper must've once rested, and I shifted uncomfortably.

"D.J.?" he asked.

"Actually, no. I really want to get into writing."

His pulse quickened. "You want to get *what* in writing?" The guy was worried that I might be litigious, and given the creepiness of a teenager meeting a grown man in a bedroom, he had reason to be scared.

"No," I clarified. "I want to get into writing as a career. Copy-writing."

"Oh," he sighed in relief. Then he rose from his desk to give me a tour.

"Come meet the staff. Helen Stanhope isn't in today, but I think everyone else is. I'm sure you know Big Todd." He pointed to a life-size cardboard standee in the kitchen of their star D.J., Big Todd. He was sipping a large mug of coffee and wore a toilet seat around his neck. The tagline read, "Number 2 in the Mornings."

"We're a pretty wild bunch," he laughed. This place was as wild as a can of Glade Cashmere Woods air freshener. At this point, I was mentally preparing to stay for the tour, then never return. But the station manager had other designs. He escorted me to the main bullpen, which was formerly the living room. There he introduced me to Victor and Laney, who worked in copywriting. Because they had opposing desks next to the fireplace, they looked like an old married couple. This despite the fact that Laney was 15 years younger than Victor and a lesbian. Laney kept a low profile, but you couldn't miss the plastic wrist brace she always wore. She said it was for the carpal tunnel she acquired at the typewriter, but based on the way she waved it in the air, maybe it was to perch her trained falcon.

"Good boy, Xerxes," she'd say while retrieving a bounty from his beak. Maybe someone's eyeballs that he pecked out at her command. Laney had that kind of vibe. Quiet but ruthless.

Victor, on the other hand, was a man in his mid-50s with a mop of red hair and sad eyes that always looked like he'd been sobbing. He reminded me of a clown. Not a harlequin or a court jester, but the trampy kind of clown you see at the circus. The kind that wears rags and carries a bindle and walks around looking heartbroken because the acrobats overhead are doing something of merit and he's just taking up oxygen. Victor wasn't just mediocre, he was aggressively mediocre. He seemed intent on proving to the world that he was the champion at being sub-par at almost everything he almost did. You could see it in the way he dressed, in his baggy cotton Dockers and cheap leather wing tips with rubber soles. You could also hear it in the jokes he cracked, which had the rhythm of a joke but not the humor. He would often interrupt a conversation to try to say something funny, but it would just lay there like a clump of dog shit ossifying on cold cement. As far as I could tell, Victor's only skill was that he could make it impossible for those around him to feel joy. I didn't think much of Victor, but I did appreciate his parents for giving him such an ironic name. I imagined them cooing over him the minute he was born.

"Honey, with our genes, this baby is never going to win anything. But wouldn't it be funny to call him Victor anyway?" And they were right. It was pretty funny.

"What's this about?" Victor mumbled to the station manager after being introduced to me. He was hunched over his desk, eating a sloppy meatball sub. His face was low and parallel to the plate, so as to not drip sauce on himself. This made it look like he wasn't eating the sub but rather giving it mouth-to-mouth, then waiting a few seconds to see if it would breathe on its own.

"He's a sophomore at Princeton," said the station manager. "He wants to be a writer."

Victor's head almost imploded under the weight of this concept, which would've scattered not his brains but a fine layer of pulverized clown dust. Thin, like talcum, which he would later scoop off the floor and use to powder his balls. Victor hated his job, and he couldn't understand why someone ... especially someone with a Princeton education ... would be dumb enough to do it for free. Although I never grew to respect Victor, I always worried that he might have a point. I think my biggest problem with him was that he enjoyed being a dream-killer. Since his dream was dead, everyone else's should be, too.

"So what are you majoring in?" he asked while licking marinara sauce from his hobo fingers.

"Well, the way things are going ... probably English literature." Even as I said it, I felt like I had admitted defeat to the powers that be in the creative writing department. I wanted to be a writer, not a reader. Victor's eyebrows raised to his greasy bangs, which were theater curtains to a matinee no one wanted to see.

"English literature?"

It was obvious Victor thought that was the most useless degree anyone could possibly earn. And again, I worried he might be right.

"Well, at least you must know the alphabet," and he handed me a crate of old tapes to sort. I spent the next hour putting them into the archives, silently singing the alphabet song because the *J* and *K* always gave me trouble. I appreciated the time alone. It afforded me a moment to consider what I had just signed up for. This radio station was just so tragic. People were pulled here by the allure of working in media. Even with the dullest imagination, it could seem fantastical. But they were moths drawn to a flame, zapped into catatonia when they realized their career was located inside a three-bedroom, two-bath with copper plumbing. That's why everyone here seemed so miserable, and I knew that if I stayed too long, I'd grow miserable, too.

"Anything else I can do?" I asked Victor later that afternoon, hoping he would say no. He was chewing on a pencil while he deliberated over some ad copy. He sighed, then glanced around the living room.

"Umm, nothing I can think of. Maybe you can polish Helen Stanhope's family crest." He let out a guffaw and Laney joined in.

"Or hold her opera glasses while she reads from the libretto."

I didn't know who Helen Stanhope was, or why she deserved

to be mocked, but I laughed anyway—eager for the approval of two people I didn't like.

When I returned the following week, Victor seemed genuinely surprised. So was I.

"Maybe he can organize the office supplies," suggested Laney.

"Sure thing!" I responded, filling the air with something unfamiliar in these parts: enthusiasm. This may have offended Laney, because as I walked away, she fired back, "By the way, Helen Stanhope was asking about you."

"Oh?"

"Yep. She was asking about you." She repeated this with a smile because it reminded herself of what joy felt like, allowing her soul to take one baby step farther away from purgatory.

This was the third time Helen Stanhope's name was brought up, and it hit me as odd that people always referred to her by both names. It made her first name sound like a title—like Duchess. But it was used ironically—a show of respect meant to be disrespectful. I considered this on my way to straighten up the office supplies. No one had to tell me where they were kept. They just had to be in the linen closet.

When I was done consolidating boxes of pens and pencils, I returned to the hearth for my next task. Victor, however, was completely tapped out of jobs for me. With nothing useless left for me to do, he finally suggested, "Do you want to, like, I dunno, write a commercial or something?"

Did I want to write a commercial or something? I couldn't believe how he de-valued writing so much that it was now equivalent to stacking bottled water in the fridge. This was the only reason why I was there. Not because I wanted to learn how to organize a closet, but because I wanted to learn how to write, even if it was from someone like Victor.

"Absolutely! What do I do?"

Victor responded as if I was a four-year-old asking how to blow on a dandelion. “You just write the commercial, that’s what you do.”

He pulled a sheet of paper from his desk and handed it to me. “Here, this one’s a 60-second spot for Ickle Pickle. It’s a deli. Mention their catered lunches.”

My mind was racing with excitement. It all seemed so literature-adjacent.

“Should there be a theme or motif?”

“Just type the thing, Hemingway.” Victor glared at me, then emphasized his disdain by honking his clown horn.

That night in my dorm room, I made an important decision. Instead of working on my final assignment for creative writing class, which would’ve meant more rejection from the faculty, I pivoted into professional writing: a radio commercial for Ickle Pickle, your neighborhood’s choice for meats and cheeses.

I stayed up late, putting as much creativity as I could into the ad copy, which I decided should be about a spy that infiltrated an international ring. Not a crime ring, but an onion ring, and it was operated out of New Delhi, spelled like the city in India. Ickle Pickle wasn’t a new deli. In fact, it had been around for generations, but I decided that if someone took me to court on that, the charges would be dismissed.

My script called for sound effects, background walla, and more accents than a tech-support call center. It was exciting and grabby and completely overwritten—like it was trying to punch its way out of my professor’s paper bag. How could you not be riveted when the world’s supply of potato salad was at stake? I wrote with one hand and used the other to pat myself on the back.

When I dropped off the script to Victor the next morning, I prefaced it with, “This is just a first draft. I’m happy to make whatever changes you want." His eyes quickly scanned the script, hopping effortlessly over the jokes that I spent so much time crafting. He nodded, then shoved it into the metal bin on his desk. Maybe I was expecting too much from Victor—that he might open his patchwork sports jacket and a dozen clowns would pour out, each one embracing me with approval. But instead he ignored me. I stood at his desk for a moment, wondering if anyone would ever want to hear the words that came out of my head.

"Now this must be our Princeton man," called a woman's voice from behind. She said it with an air of aristocracy, and I knew this could be only one person: Helen Stanhope. I turned to discover a matronly woman in her mid-60s, sipping a cup of tea while delicately holding a saucer just below. Her bleached-blonde hair was piled high, like shoveled snow on a bank, and held in place by royal decree.

"Helen Stanhope," she said, offering her hand.

I glanced at Victor. His translucent skin was fracturing under the pressure of jubilation. This must've been the moment he'd been waiting for—when he'd sacrifice me to Helen Stanhope.

"Helen is the host of *Princeton's Talking*," he said. It was a radio program about local culture, but he slurred the words together so it sounded like "Princeton Stalking," a call-in show for serial killers. As I later discovered, Helen was a big benefactor to the radio station, and in exchange for her generous donations, she was given a weekly time slot, even though her show barely had any listeners. This made the staff resentful of her, like she didn't deserve the honor of her words being heard. That's what we had in common.

"Do you listen to my program?" Helen asked, almost rhetorically. I had never heard of *Princeton's Talking*, but if I had, it's not something I would've listened to, even if you cut holes in my earlobes and wired them with car speakers.

"I will now," I responded politely. That was good enough for Helen Stanhope, and she smiled while squeezing lemon into her teacup.

"Come, let's to the lanai," she said. I didn't know what a lanai was, but I was certain her sentence was missing a verb. Let's what to the lanai? Let's *go* to the lanai? Let's *sashay* to the lanai? Let's *bring a translator* for you and I to the lanai? But that was Helen, always using language as a way of transporting her somewhere else. A trunk was a *portmanteau,* a suitcase was a *valise,* and a couch was a *davenport.* It was pretentious and alienating, and I found all of it to be incredibly amusing.

"Yes, my good man," Victor added. "By all means, walk the grounds." He smiled coquettishly, then squirted water from the flower on his lapel.

I followed Helen downstairs to the main level, where she pulled open the sliding door to the backyard. She marveled at the view, as if it were the Gardens of Versailles instead of what it was —a patch of grass where an old swing set was decaying. I wondered if Helen Stanhope was aware that Victor, and everyone else at the station, made fun of her. Was she taking the high road by ignoring them, or was she completely oblivious? Either way, Helen was unlike anyone else there. Whereas they saw the radio station as the shithole that it was, Helen saw what she wanted to see—grandeur. She lived in the fantasy of radio and was as crazy as Don Quixote.

"I understand you're an English major," she said while pulling a chair from the patio set. She accented the word "major," which made it sound like I was an officer in the British Army. An English *major.* Practically a war hero.

"I'll probably concentrate in the plays of Shakespeare," I said, sensing that this detail would impress her.

"How marvelous! You'll have to give me your thoughts on *Henry IV, Part 2.*"

I didn't have thoughts on any of the *Henry* parts, and if I did, I couldn't imagine having enough to spare. But I didn't want to disappoint her, so I steered the conversation to *Hamlet,* which I read not in college, but in my senior year of high school. And it was the Cliffs Notes version. Still, it really perked her up.

"Alas, poor Yorick!" she quoted. "I knew him, Horatio." She then fell silent for a moment while dramatically gazing at the citronella candle on the picnic table, as if it were a skull and she was mourning poor Yorick. I felt awkward watching her, unsure if I should console her or just let her grieve in peace. What are you supposed to do when someone departs reality like that? Do you just watch them go, or do you follow them out of curiosity or politeness? Strangely, I decided to follow. Not in this moment, but a few minutes later I did.

Helen broke her silence, and the conversation grew light again. As we spoke, it became clear that Helen was fascinated by my life, especially when I talked about my aspirations. Her face lit up when I mentioned I wanted to be a television writer, as if my success was already a done deal. Part of me loved that. It was flattering to have her attention, and she spoke to me so warmly, like we were old friends. She was an adult treating me not like a child but like an equal. That's a powerful thing. But her exuberance also made me feel guilty. I clarified that I didn't really see a path forward for me, given that I'd already been rejected from the creative writing program not once but twice. I thought this would put an end to this conversation. Maybe she'd offer some half-hearted encouragement or greeting-card platitude about the importance of never giving up, and then we'd both give up. But

Helen, mounted on her faithful steed of self-delusion, just galloped ahead.

"And what kind of television show will you write?"

"It'll be science fiction," I wanted to say. "Just like this conversation we're having." But instead, I took a giant leap. I humored her—going down a path that, in my mind, I had no right going down. And the minute I said it, I felt like a fraud who would one day be exposed.

"Sitcoms," I responded.

"I love that!" applauded Helen. "I used to watch *My Mother the Car*. Do you remember that one?" Actually, I didn't. It was probably 30 years before my time, but I nodded in agreement.

"Heavens, it's getting late," she said. "I have to be on-air soon, but you must pay me a visit some time." She reached into her purse and pulled out a fountain pen, although a quill wouldn't have been unexpected. Then, with her well-practiced longhand, she wrote her home address on a piece of personalized stationery.

"How does this Saturday at three sound?"

This was the third invitation Helen offered me. The first was going to the lanai. And the second was for me to pretend that I was someone I wasn't—an important and gifted writer. This would become a pattern with Helen. She was always inviting me deeper into her world of make-believe, refusing to step foot in mine.

"Yes, that sounds ... marvelous," I responded, still getting the hang of this sophisticated-socialite thing. I'm certain I glowed with dignity, which is something that I had been lacking of late.

She gave me her card, and I guarded it carefully in my hands, as if it were a ticket to my own coronation. And with that, Helen the Duchess of Witherspoon returned inside to commence her high-society call-in show, from the children's bedroom off the hallway.

* * *

Helen Stanhope lived on the outskirts, just before the town became farmland. During the drive there, the excitement of accepting this invitation began to wane. It was weird enough to be socializing with an actual socialite, but the fact that she was old enough to be my grandmother made it weirder still. We had so little in common. I was nothing like Helen, and Helen was nothing like herself. The pea gravel that lined her long driveway must've agreed, because it chattered underneath the wheels of my car like milk on Rice Krispies.

"It's not too late to turn around," it mumbled.

"I'm capable of making my own decisions, Pea Gravel."

"Just be careful," it urged. "You have no idea what you're getting into."

I had to admit, Pea Gravel was making a good point. I was still a child, entering an adult's world. But Helen, in sharp contrast to Victor and Laney, was so friendly and warm. Yes, she was strange enough to almost be fictitious, but what harm could come from spending an hour or so with her? She was delightful and interesting, and nothing about it felt inappropriate at all, and nothing was.

The house was a stately old Colonial and perfectly symmetrical, so that if you liked one side, it saved you the trouble of looking at the other. It had hedges that were manicured into spheres and cubes, so that, like Helen, they no longer resembled anything you might find in nature. There was no servant to announce my presence, but there probably would've been had I arrived 10 minutes and 200 years earlier. Also very Helen-like was the fact that her house didn't have a doorbell. Instead there was a large brass knocker. It had a lion's head with a ring in its mouth. Knockers are a test. If you don't bang hard enough, the occupant won't hear you. But if you do, you're basically yelling, "Open the fucking door!" I tried to find just the right knock.

"Ah, you've made it," cried Helen from afar. A moment later, she greeted me at the door. "Come in. I have tea and *petit fours.*"

I knew what tea was. I mean, I'm not an idiot. But *petit fours* was anyone's guess. It was bad enough that Helen insisted on communicating in Victorian English, but now French? Turns out I had nothing to worry about. *Petit fours* were just fancy cookies.

I admit it was pretty flattering to be served fancy cookies. When I was a child, my mother used to bring out assorted Pepperidge Farm cookies whenever we had guests. "Company" is what she called them, as if our family was lonely—stranded on a desert island. In a way, we were. My parents were very loving and supportive people. Their children always came first. But dealing with difficult emotions wasn't their strong suit. If we had a family crest, like Helen did, our motto would've been "Get over it." So that's why we all sat alone in our pain, waiting for someone, anyone, to arrive and rescue us. "Thank God company is coming over!"

My mother kept these cookies in the pantry, and under no circumstances were we allowed to eat them for ourselves. So if I wanted one, I'd have to wait for company to arrive. The packaging described the cookies as "distinctive," and they were sold in something that resembled a jewelry box. Lifting the cardboard lid revealed a cellophane window that protected the cookies underneath, like diamond rings in a display case. Moments after our guest sat down, I'd do a cat-burglar drop from the ceiling, snatch a paper doily full of Milanos, and scamper away. That left everyone else with those horrible chocolate cookies, which tasted like they were made from the green dust janitors used to clean up vomit. And now here I was, 10 years later, someone else's company, pretending to be worthy of such a fancy cookie.

"How's school treating you?" cried Helen from the kitchen while she prepared a tray.

"You know ... it's hard." I responded from her parlor, which was both dark and velvety. It had a stillness, her house, and you could hear it loudly between the ticks of her grandfather clock standing in the corner. Tick ... Tick ... It dripped time like it was trying to get a confession out of me. I knew what it wanted to hear, but I was unwilling to say it out loud.

As I waited for Helen to enter with the tea kettle, my eyes scanned the room. There were photos of her when she was younger—too many of them. These were pictures of travel and life events. Some were intimate and others were public. Some of them hung on the walls, not in a pattern, but scattered like buck-shot. Others were perched on shelves in expensive silver frames, crowding each other to get to the front. They were as dramatic as Helen. From the pieces that I saw of her life, I was certain that Helen was once married, and that her husband must've died years ago. I could feel the absence in this room, but not the grief. That had long since been tamed and domesticated. For all her social-izing and theatricality, I finally got a read on Helen. She was lonely.

"You know, I absolutely loved that spot you wrote for Ickle Pickle," she said, bounding into the room. The scent of chamomile and cookies respectfully trailed two steps behind her.

"Oh, you read it?"

"No, I heard it in my automobile yesterday."

That came as news, and it shook me. Victor never once mentioned my script. I didn't even know he liked it, much less thought it was worthy of producing. I should've been excited to learn that it was now being broadcast over the airwaves, but I wasn't. I was hurt. Even though it was just a commercial, this was a big deal for me. It was validation. It was proof that words that I had put onto a page had value. And now they felt worthless and disposable. My mood immediately soured. I think Helen could tell, because she dramatically crossed to the bookshelf, as if compelled by a fiction larger than both of us.

"You know," she said, "I think you'd make a wonderful guest on my program. We can talk about your writing career."

It's amazing how quickly my disposition changed when Helen offered to put a microphone in front of me. I felt important. Like I had a voice. And I answered enthusiastically, as if words had never before come out of my mouth.

"I'd love to!"

The following Sunday, I rode my bike downhill to the radio station. I was wearing dress shoes and an itchy sweater that I reserved for special occasions. Together, they made me feel like a person of note. I pedaled slowly so that others could enjoy me as well. I was on cloud nine. Someone had decided that my voice was worthy of being heard. I was a person who could put words on a page that would move people. They would then thank me for having entertained them but also for illuminating their own lives. I was a writer now.

Parking my bike outside the radio station, I no longer saw it as a house on Witherspoon Street. I saw it the way Helen Stanhope saw it. It was now a high-rise on Madison Avenue. The sticky carpet in the entranceway had been replaced by a marble floor worthy of my feet. I stood tall, almost regal, as I entered the station. On my way to the recording booth, I was surprised to find Victor at the water cooler, still hunched over from his long commute in a tiny clown car.

"What are you doing here on a Sunday?" he asked.

"Helen Stanhope's having me on her show," I said proudly. "I'm going to talk about my writing." I said it loud enough to echo off the refrigerator, and when it hit my ears, I almost shivered with excitement. Victor, who I assumed would melt with jealousy, didn't have the same reaction. Instead, a puzzled look came to his face.

"You're going to talk about your *writing?*" he asked, sincerely. "What writing?"

I jolted, the way you do when you dream you're falling. It was such an obvious response, yet hearing it from Victor made me realize the stupidity of my own words. "Yeah, what writing?!" Was it the commercial I wrote for the local deli? Or was it the various short stories I submitted that left my professors feeling unfulfilled. Victor was right. Leave it to the fool to show us our folly. I wasn't a writer. I was nothing close to it. And here I was, caught up in the fantasy that Helen had created for me. I had accepted yet another invitation from her, only this time there would be consequences. Consequences from the public upon discovering my delusions. The blood drained from my face, and I became as white as the greasepaint on Victor's cheeks. Now we were both clowns.

I walked slowly to the recording booth, still stunned by the realization that I was a fraud who was now walking into a trap. Helen waved to me from down the hall. She was standing next to the ON AIR sign, the meaning of which suddenly became obvious to me: "on air," as in "not grounded" or "putting on airs."

"Michael!" she exclaimed, pulling me inside and shutting the door behind us. The room was padded with thick foam, making it feel a holding cell for the insane. The minute the door shut, all the small sounds in the room simply vanished, creating a space that was eerily silent. It reminded me of Helen's living room, where the photos on her shelves pushed each other out of the way to be seen.

"Are you excited?" she asked, her words creating a ripple in the calm. She handed me a set of earphones, and I nodded unconvincingly as I put them on. I was almost surprised that they fit, given how big my head was only a few minutes earlier.

"How close am I supposed to get to this thing?" I asked, nervously sliding my chair toward the microphone. I could've just as easily been referring to the truth. How close should I get to it? Do I go on-air and play along with this charade, or just call the whole thing off?

Helen fiddled with some knobs and buttons, flicking some on while turning others off. It looked like she was prepping a plane before takeoff. Everything seemed complicated and cumbersome, and for a moment, I felt like I'd been given a reprieve—that maybe this whole radio interview would be too difficult to get off the ground. I could reschedule. Or maybe never schedule at all. Before I could even entertain that possibility, the red ON AIR light came on, and Helen introduced me to her audience. I tried to convince myself that no one would be listening to me, since no one ever did. But there had to be a few. Dozens? Hundreds? I couldn't see them, and I couldn't hear them. But they must there. And soon they'd be judging me, and rightfully so.

"I'm here with my guest, writer *extraordinaire* Michael Jamin —a sophomore at Princeton University." My heart was racing now.

"Creative Writing Program reject," I wanted to clarify. Helen continued to heap praise on me while quoting lines from my commercial, as if it were in contention for a literary award. I cringed when she asked me how many ideas I came up with before landing on the premise that I used. Just one. Was I supposed to give it more thought? Helen was so excited and so proud of me, and yet I just wanted her to shut up. While the hyperboles leaped off her tongue, I decided that I had learned a valuable lesson: that I would never talk about my future until it was my present. From this moment forward, if there was a version of me that I wanted to live, I wouldn't share it. I'd keep that secret locked inside my own dark and velvety parlor. In other words, I'd leave Helen behind and live in reality.

As she spoke, I glanced at my watch, mentally willing time to move faster. Six minutes left. Five minutes left. Just when I thought I might escape with my dignity, my biggest fear came true—the phone bank at Helen's side lit up. First one line. Then two more. They were listeners on the other end, eager to call me out for my grandiose bullshittery. The phone blinked incessantly, demanding to be acknowledged, like Helen's grandfather clock. I became obsessed, my eyes nervously checking it every few seconds. What was Helen going to do? Would she pick it up, allowing the caller to expose me on-air? And if so, would she defend me, because that would only make things worse. I was mad at her for preying on my ego this way—for setting me up to be publicly shamed just so that I would participate in her crazy little socialite game. I mean, who does that to a kid?! But then Helen did something completely unexpected. Without ever breaking eye contact, she leaned in toward the microphone, putting her body between me and the phone bank, so that I couldn't see the flashing lights.

"Stay here," her eyes smiled. "Please, just stay here with me." This time, it didn't feel like an invitation. It felt like she was pleading with me not leave.

For all I know, the phone continued to blink for the rest of the interview, but she never took any calls.

* * *

The walk back to my dorm room after my near miss with humiliation felt especially far. It was mostly uphill, and I was now carrying the weight of my useless bicycle on my shoulders. This was my fault. I enjoyed the ride downhill while it lasted, but the price for that had to be paid. It's something you don't think about when you're wrapped up in the fantasy. Along the way, I tried to make sense out of Helen Stanhope, but I was too young to have any understanding. It was this same lack of understanding that was always missing from my creative writing pieces. I couldn't figure characters' motivations out, and I couldn't figure Helen out, so I stopped trying. Instead, I decided I should sweep this horribly embarrassing experience under the rug, pretending it never happened. And that's what I did. I never talked about it, I never returned to the radio station, and I never saw my friend Helen again. I heard she died years later.

I'm ashamed that I just disappeared from her life that way. It was wrong and selfish. I imagine it hurt her feelings the same way it hurt her feelings to be mocked by the station employees. And now I was no better than them.

On the occasions that I allowed myself, I'd think of Helen Stanhope and circle back to that big question: Why did she hype me up that way? What function did I serve in her odd world of make-believe? Was I simply there to keep her company? At first, I thought it was because I was a student at Princeton, and therefore a man of letters, worthy to be in her presence. But that never felt right. As I got older, I decided it was the excitement of my youth that she was feeding off—when all the photos of your life haven't yet been taken. That wasn't it, either.

It's only recently, when I got much closer to Helen's age, that I realized I'd been looking at it all wrong. Helen didn't want anything from me, and how foolish I was to think that she ever did. She was giving me something. And amazingly, it was the only thing I wanted. Somehow she understood why it was important for me to be a writer in the first place—so that I could make sense of the loneliest thoughts inside me, share them with the world, and maybe feel like I had company too. Quietly, in between the ticks of her grandfather clock and flashes on her phone bank, Helen did just that. She heard me. And now I can hear her.

"But of course you became a television writer!" she laughs. "Was there ever any doubt?" Then Helen, Duchess of Witherspoon, raises her teacup and proposes a toast. And I laugh, too.

Swing and a Ms.

I had just finished slow-dancing with a bridesmaid when my sister pulled me aside. Her face was red from embarrassment.

"What the hell were you doing out there?" she whispered sternly.

"What do you mean?"

"You're supposed to be slow-dancing, not rocking side to side like you're on a ship at high seas. You have to lead."

"We were co-leading."

"Jesus, you're an adult now. Take a dance class and get it together, will ya?"

It was a slap in the face, but my sister was right. I really had no idea what I was doing out there, but I definitely didn't want to take dance classes. That felt way too grown up. Even though I was 23 and on my own, I was still clinging to the idea of being a kid. It's why I used a milk crate for a nightstand despite the fact that nothing could rest on it without falling through the holes. It's also why I slept on a cheap futon that resembled a doggie bed. I wasn't ready to have adult things.

On the flight home from the wedding, I got a seat in the emergency row with extra legroom. Instead of being squished like a chick inside a box of Easter Peeps, I could stretch out a little. I could actually see my feet. My clumsy, non-dancing feet. I crossed my ankles and tucked them back underneath the chair.

The flight attendant, a tall brunette who looked great even in her thick polyester uniform, approached me. "Are you comfortable —"

"Oh my God, I'm *so* comfortable. Thank you!"

"I wasn't done. Are you comfortable assisting other passengers —"

"I guess. What do they need?"

"Please, just let me finish. Are you comfortable assisting other passengers in the event of an emergency landing?" She said it quickly, so that I wouldn't interrupt her.

"There's gonna be an emergency landing?"

"No, sir. In the event."

I thought about my crossed ankles, and how it made me feel ladylike. I uncrossed them and planted them firmly in front of me. Like a man's man. So macho.

"Yeah, I'm comfortable."

She smiled weakly and continued down the aisle. It struck me how she called me "sir." She saw me as a man—maybe it was time for me to see myself that way. I could take that leap, and I bet I could pull it off, too. A half-hour later, she returned and asked the man next to me if he wanted something to drink.

"Gin and tonic."

"And you, sir?" she said, looking at me.

"Tell me more about your apple juice. Does it come with a sippy straw?"

"Yes, it comes with a sippy straw."

"Very good then."

* * *

The dance studio I found was in a commercial building not far from where I lived. The bottom floor was occupied by a dry cleaner, and the studio had the top floor. It struck me as a symbiotic relationship. You could pick up your clean, blousy, sequin-covered leotard on the way to your samba lesson, bump and grind for an hour and half, then drop it off on the way out, all sweaty and gross. Being on the top floor, the studio had three oversize windows facing the street. I'd driven by countless times, mocking the foolish few who were willing to humiliate themselves by dancing in a window. "Are they aware that's not one-way glass?" I scoffed. And now, here I was, about to become one of them.

Leading to it was a long staircase that was narrow and steep. I didn't know what adulthood would look like, but I had a feeling that I'd find it at the top. I paused to consider if this was something I really wanted to do. I didn't. But I went up anyway, taking each step one at a time to delay the inevitable.

At the top of the stairs was the front office, which was little more than a tiny room with half-doors at its entrance. Dutch doors, I think they call them. The kind they use in sitcoms because they're funny to look at. The bottom one was kept closed and the top opened, so that the door was neither open nor shut. It was something in between. The owners, a husband-and-wife team, sat hunched over a small, gray cashbox counting the day's receipts. Judging by the amount of money in it, it didn't strike me as a two-person job.

"What made you decide to take up dancing?" asked the wife.

"My sister made fun of me at a wedding."

The husband nodded. It was a story he must've heard a thousand times. I wondered if anyone here was taking dance lessons voluntarily.

I signed up for a bloc of 10 classes at a discounted rate, and paid by pulling out my credit card, which made me feel more mature than I wanted to be.

"What do you want to study?" asked the husband. "Salsa, swing, tango ... "

"Which is the one you do at a wedding?"

It was almost imperceptible, but I picked up on it. The wife cringed.

They pointed me in the direction of the main studio—the one with the giant windows facing the street. It was a cavernous room, with ballet barres against the walls and plenty of open space to fill with humiliation. It was a beginners class, and a dozen or so students waited anxiously for the instructor to arrive. Cutout footprints were scattered about so that students could practice their footwork. When I entered, the clop-clopping of my shoes against the hardwood floor caused everyone to turn their heads toward me. First they smiled nervously, thinking I might be the instructor. That look turned into disappointment when it became obvious I wasn't. I'd let them down, just by being me.

I walked to the rear of the class, thinking that's where I could hide, and caught my reflection bouncing infinitely inside the three giant mirrors covering the walls of the studio. There I am on the right looking awkward, there I am on the left looking awkward, and there's one million of me straight ahead, looking back at me while I'm trying to vanish.

"*Estamos listos!*" shouted a handsome man in his mid-30s. He was our instructor, Joseba, and I came to discover that he always wore silk shirts and leather dance slippers—his body glazed in a half-inch layer of cologne, like melted sugar on a doughnut. He glided into the room as if riding atop a chariot. It was effortless, and dramatic, and you could smell him through the walls.

"There is nothing sexier than knowing how to dance," Joseba shouted over the music as he gyrated his pelvis. "If it's men or women that you desire, soon you'll have more than you'll know what to do with." I giggled.

His promise sounded like the introduction to an infomercial—too good to be true. Hitting on women wasn't easy for me. It was confidence that I lacked. I wasn't built like an athlete, or handsome like a model. I was only me. I figured most women could size me up with just a glance, and if they got close enough, they could actually hear the insecurities shouting in my head. A pretender. A dreamer. A fraud. Better to keep them at arm's length, so they couldn't learn this about me.

"In dance," proclaimed Joseba, "the man leads and the Betty follows." A "Betty" is what he called a woman. If that was chauvinistic, he didn't seem concerned, and he took it one step further by grabbing a woman's hand without asking. It belonged to a woman he had never met, and he pulled her tight against his body. I was shocked.

"In order to be led," he continued, "the woman must make a frame with her torso and arms." He lifted her right arm high into the air, and placed her left hand just behind his shoulder.

"That way the man can steer her, just like steering a car." I couldn't believe he was comparing women to automobiles. I thought about gasping, then looked around at some of the women in the class. No one seemed to be offended, so I figured maybe he knew what he was talking about.

"So much about life is knowing how to lead." I zoned out for that part. I was here to pick up dance moves, not gain profound self-knowledge. I turned my attention to one of my bazillion reflections in the mirror, who weren't paying attention, either. Maybe that's why he singled me out.

"Now you lead me," he said, taking my hand and pulling me into the middle of the dance floor. I wasn't ready for that.

"It's going to be okay," I told myself. "No one's watching. Just a handful of people in this class ... and everyone driving by on the street below."

"Bring me in tight," barked Joseba. "Tighter! Tighter still!"

He yanked me in, so close that our male parts were practically starting a friction fire. I could now smell the gum in his mouth. Spearmint.

"Our junk is pretty close, don't you think?" I asked, uncomfortably.

"That's why they call it 'ballroom,' *mi amor.* There's not a lot of room for our balls." He listened to the music, waited for the top of the measure, then off we went. Just two men dancing in the window of a second-story walk-up.

Within moments, we were gliding across the room. Like Fred Astaire and Ginger from *Gilligan's Island.* When I pushed, he spun on a dime. When I pulled, he reeled toward me, then passed beneath my arm. It was like working a puppet—he was on display, yet I was the one in control. I could've danced for hours with this guy.

"You're an amazing dancer," I confessed, completely impressed with the person he allowed himself to be. Joseba just smiled and said nothing. He didn't need to be told by me—he knew it. When the music ended, he had me dip him just a few inches above the floor, and our eyes locked.

"How's that?" I asked.

"Now wink at me," he whispered.

"Wink at you?"

"Trust."

It made no sense, but fine, I winked at him, and the class burst into applause.

That week, I returned two more times, and the following week, every other day. At the dance studio that I used to deride mercilessly, I quickly became one of the regulars. If this was adulthood, then I'd been afraid of it for absolutely no reason.

In time, I grew into a really good swing dancer—a guy who knew where to move, and trusted his feet to get him there. It would've been completely transformational if not for the fact that, by day, I was still a meek office assistant. I worked for two television writers as an errand boy, basically. In the morning, I brewed them coffee in a pot I only said I washed. And in the afternoon, I got them lunch. In between, I had almost nothing to do, but on the rare occasions they'd assign me another task, I became resentful.

"Seriously? You're gonna make me put paper in the copy machine now?"

Part of the problem was that I didn't have an adult job yet. I was in limbo—waiting for the future to punch my dance card. So I just sat at my desk, staring into the distance while I secretly rehearsed my footwork below. "Left, right, backstep." While practicing, I'd often think about the promise Joseba made on that first day of class—that dancing would make me instantly attractive to women. I wanted to believe him, but I also wanted to prove him wrong.

As part of my daily work routine, I'd find an excuse to walk to the supply closet on the other side of the floor. Often it was just to grab a box of brads, which is what they call the brass fasteners used to hold scripts together. Most of the other offices were vacant, and seeing them made me feel vacant, too. Why was I the only one wasting time here? But the supply closet was full of paper and pens and highlighters. In contrast to the empty offices, it felt lush. Like Tahiti for middle management. For some reason, standing in the supply closet and looking at boxes of manila folders cheered me up. Walking there took me past Nicole's office, who was one of the few tenants on my floor. She was five or six years older than me, and pretty, with sandy-blonde hair and green eyes that saw more than I could see. She worked as a set designer. Unlike me, she was successful and powerful. She had an office with a window. I had a cubicle with a view of the recycling bin.

The first few times I passed Nicole, I said nothing. I was too intimidated—like I didn't deserve to talk to her. But one time, after stealing a ream of copy paper from the show she worked on, she called off to me, "Why are you stealing my paper?"

"Well ... because I told my bosses that I ordered some, but I never got around to it because it was pretty much the only thing I had to do that day."

Nicole laughed, and for a second I felt good about myself.

After that first encounter, I slowed down whenever I passed her office, hoping that she'd notice me. But more to the point, I was hoping that anyone would notice me. I felt so invisible at that time. I never spoke to Nicole, though. And she never spoke to me. She just acknowledged me with a faint smile.

"Salad, huh?" she asked one afternoon, finally breaking our stalemate. I was holding a tray of food from the commissary.

"It's for my boss." The minute I said it, I regretted it, realizing how subservient it made me look. And that wasn't even the half of it. My salary was so low, I couldn't even afford to eat lunch at the commissary. I brought peanut-butter-and-jelly sandwiches from home, like a third-grader.

"So you're getting lunch for the boss. Any other big plans for today?" she joked. I didn't want her to make fun of me, so I beat her to the punch, proving to her and everyone else that I understood my place in the world.

"Since you ask, this afternoon I'll be patching through some very important phone calls. Lots of them. More than *you'll* ever patch through." I leaned against her doorframe, trying hard to look cool. It was uncomfortable against my shoulder, and I wondered how long I could hold this pose. Thirty seconds? No, maybe 10.

"You'd better get going, then." She smiled coyly.

"Nah, I'm training my bosses to answer the phones themselves." In the distance, I heard an office phone ring. I could tell it wasn't theirs, but I instinctively lurched forward. My reaction was Pavlovian and emasculating, and it reminded me that I had no business talking to this woman.

Nicole pushed her chair away from her desk, and pulled her feet in to sit cross-legged. That became her go-to pose, and it projected authority, especially with her sitting and me standing before her.

"So what's your story?" she asked. That's code in Hollywood. It's what you ask someone with a job like waiter or clerk, sensing that they aspire to do something more. I hated that question because the answer made me feel like a fool. Screenwriter. The odds of that happening were so remote—I sounded like a child with a daydream. I shared it with her anyway. To say nothing would've been sadder.

"Good for you," she said, without a hint of condescension. It was like she was giving me permission to be the person that I wanted to be. I was uncomfortable with that because it felt like a lie, so I excused myself and returned to my desk. But her encouragement made me want to visit her again. It was complicated, being offered a choice like that—standing before a door that was neither opened nor closed. Like a Dutch door. I didn't know how to go forward.

Driving back to my apartment that night, I thought about

Nicole's green eyes smiling at me from behind her desk. Thinking about her outside of work was something I hadn't done before, and it felt like I was bringing her home with me. It was almost intimate. I thought about her even as I parked my car and sauntered down the cement pathway to my apartment. But that stopped the minute I opened the door to my dingy studio apartment, with the milk-crate nightstand and futon bed. Suddenly, I didn't want her here.

The next day at the office, maybe out of boredom, I allowed myself to daydream again. I let my feet dance beneath my desk ... just as long as no one could see them. During my afternoon run to the supply closet, I found a shovel hiding behind the plastic trash cans. Who knows why it was there—maybe someone buried an actor—but I picked it up and carried it past Nicole's office, slowing down just long enough for her to notice.

"Why are you carrying a shovel?" she asked.

"Oh, this? I'm digging a pool beside my desk," I bragged. "I just think it'll be easier for me to write with my feet dipped in the water.

"Good idea," laughed Nicole.

"You don't think it's foolish, do you? Digging a pool inside of an office building?"

"No. Not at all."

We stared at each other for a beat, lingering just a little too long. This time I broke the silence.

"You should come over for a swim sometime. You know, if Human Resources doesn't shut it down." With that one line I took a giant step forward. I was flirting with an adult—someone outside my bracket. It felt bold, and it surprised me.

"Maybe I will," she smiled.

A few nights later, as I was sneaking out early for my dance class, Nicole stopped me at the door.

"What's with the shoes?" she asked, pointing to the ones poking out of my bag. They had leather soles and were easier to dance in. Again I thought of lying to her, and again I told the truth.

"Swing class," I said, almost apologetically.

"You take dance lessons?"

"Yeah. My sister made fun of me at a wedding."

I thought for sure that Nicole would laugh at me, seeing me once again me for who I really was—-the man who was still a boy. But instead she leaned back in her chair, pulled her feet in and thought for a moment.

"I want to go."

Nicole arrived to class late, while I was dancing with a 60-year-old Russian woman whose name I could never pronounce. Back at the office, I warned Nicole about the fishbowl windows at the dance studio, but that didn't seem to faze her. Nothing ever seemed to faze her. But now that she was actually stepping onto the wooden floor, a beginner in a dance class, I could tell that she was self-conscious. I had the same look on my face a few months earlier.

I waved Nicole over. Her eyes turned to relief as she crossed to my side. Up until now, it hadn't occurred to me that the dance studio was my turf, and that this would do more than make us equals. If anything, I was the one now in charge. That became obvious when the music started playing.

"I don't know what to do," she said apprehensively.

"You don't have to know what to do," I said. "I do."

Then I grabbed her hand, without even asking her, and I pulled her toward the center of the room. Her hand was soft, and immediately wrapped itself around mine, like we were lovers vacationing on a tropical island. It was the first time I had ever touched her, and yet I did it without thinking. It was the same way I handled all the women in the class. It was just something you needed to do if you wanted to dance. I showed Nicole how to frame her body, stiff enough so that I could control where she goes. Like a car. On the first beat, I pulled her in tight against my body, and her eyes lit up with excitement. I could feel her warm breath against my cheek, and I liked it there. But then, just as quickly, I pushed her away and that took her by surprise. She was intrigued. I was driving now.

She got the basic steps pretty fast, and it wasn't long before I was leading her into more complicated turns, wrapping her arm around my chest and then my neck as I brought her in closer and closer, then pushed her away again.

"Oh my God," she blushed when the music ended and I dipped her to the floor. "You really know what you're doing!"

I did, and I winked at her. I actually winked at her. I never do that—that's not who I am. It felt good to be this person. Not the phone boy, but someone better than that. When the hour was over, Nicole and I walked down to our cars.

"What are you doing Friday night?" she asked.

"I don't know. Laundry? Vacuuming? I'm keeping my options open."

"You should come over," she said, touching my chest. She'd had her arms around me all evening while we danced, but this felt different, and it startled me. Her invitation was completely unexpected. It hadn't occurred to me that we might've been on a first date. She had paid for this class herself—all $10 of it.

"Yeah." I replied. "That sounds great."

Nicole lived in my neighborhood about a half-mile from my place. In Los Angeles, a half-mile is considered too far to walk, so when Friday night came, I got in my car and drove for two minutes. The parking signs were different on her street, with confusing restrictions and exemptions. Rather than try to decipher it all, I decided to just drive around in wider and wider concentric circles until I finally found a sign-less spot halfway between my apartment and hers. I locked my car and hoofed it the rest of the way.

I was carrying a bottle of red wine. I bought it because I didn't want to show up empty-handed, and wine seemed more sophisticated than a bag of potato chips. The problem is, I didn't know how to hold the bottle. It was heavy and awkward. In someone else's hands it would've belonged, but in mine it felt like a prop for a different character. Carrying it from the bottom made me feel like a waiter at a five-star restaurant. Pretentious but also subservient. Grabbing it from the neck, though, made me feel like a caveman wielding a club. The fact that I didn't know how to hold a bottle of wine should've been a warning to me.

"You didn't walk here, did you?" asked Nicole, when I finally arrived.

"Of course not." That was a half-lie.

"Come on in," she said casually. Her feet were bare, and she wore loose-fitting cotton pants that were cuffed high above her ankles. There wasn't any nervousness in her eyes. She looked relaxed, as if she were on a beach instead of here with me—just splashing around her life.

"Ooh, vino!" said Nicole, seeing the bottle in my hand. She retreated to the kitchen to pull some glasses. I used this time to take in her apartment. It was a 1920s Spanish duplex, with thick stucco walls and wood-beam ceilings. A balcony overlooked a courtyard, where a fountain took you to the markets of Andalusia. It was wonderful. The inside of her apartment I can only describe as "decorated." With her grown-up money, Nicole had purchased artwork and real furniture made from wood and not milk crates. It all seemed so mature. I lived in a rectangular shitbox with blank, white walls. It was a canvas that I was afraid to paint.

"Here, you open it," said Nicole, handing me a corkscrew before disappearing into her bedroom. It's funny how that part surprised me. I guess I didn't actually think we'd drink the wine. It was just an offering, and I assumed she'd throw it on a shelf somewhere and forget all about it. But now I had a corkscrew in my hand. There, taking in Nicole's very grown-up life, an unfamiliar feeling washed over me. Obviously, I'd seen corkscrews before. They were fun. With their swiveling heads and arms that could rise high into the air, they looked like victims of a stickup. But corkscrews were something a mother or father would own, and here I was being given one by a peer. Despite having spent my youth wondering what adulthood would look like, I didn't expect it to look like a woman handing me a corkscrew.

The transition seemed so abrupt, like jumping into a pool. One moment I was a kid, and the next I wasn't. This should have been exciting, but instead my heart dipped. The cold, metal point of the corkscrew dug into the heel of my palm, and it was uncomfortable. My adolescence was over now, and I never got a chance to say goodbye.

"There's glasses on the counter," yelled Nicole from afar.

I cautiously found my way to her kitchen, which was next to the dining room, exactly where one might expect to find it. In my studio apartment, the kitchen was next to the bathroom because no one would think to put one there and everyone loves a surprise. There were photos on her refrigerator held by magnets. I never even thought of buying refrigerator magnets. I didn't have lots of spending money, and I guess magnets seemed— I don't know—decadent.

"What should we drink to?" said Nicole, returning from her

bedroom. She was holding a joint to her mouth, her lips pressed into a kiss.

"Umm ... "

I had nothing to say at this moment, shocked that casual drinking had somehow escalated into recreational marijuana use. I was right to equate this to jumping into a pool, because now I was in over my head, frantically paddling to stay afloat.

"Let's sit," she said, taking my hand the way I took her hand on the dance floor. Then she lead me to the shallow end by the sofa. I stared at the joint she was holding, pretending not to be shocked.

We sat on the couch a few feet apart, and I shifted my weight so I could rest my arm on the back of the cushion. I thought this would make me look empowered—like this was just another evening for me, hanging out with a fellow adult, sitting on real furniture and using corkscrews. Nicole took a hit, her chest expanding toward me as it filled with smoke. I watched her, captivated, like she was onstage for a show I was just old enough to get into. She leaned over and extended the joint to me. In so doing, the top of her blouse swung open, as if offering me a choice: the joint or what was behind Button No. 2. My eyes went down her shirt, but fast, so that I wouldn't get caught.

"I, uh ... I've never really smoked one of those."

"Never?" she said. Her face lit up with delight. "Not even once?"

I shook my head no, and maybe the rest of my body, too.

"Don't worry. I'll show you." She handed me the joint, and I pinched it hard, like a lobster grabbing a chef's nose in a cartoon.

"Just breath in. But not too much."

"Like this?" I asked, while demonstrating what it's like to breathe, but without actually inhaling any smoke.

"Yep, that's how you do it." I smiled, almost proud of myself for knowing how to breathe. Then I took a hit of marijuana. Just a small one. A child's portion, you might say. Over my cough, I pushed out the words "Am I high yet?"

"No," she laughed. Then she reached over my body to grab the stereo remote, offering me the same view once again. And once again I took the bait. This time I held my gaze for a half-second longer, and when she caught me looking, she smiled.

Her sofa was a sectional. Cream-colored. It was expensive and plush, not like my shitty futon—the one with the mattress that sagged off the frame like it was running away in embarrassment. My finger traced the ridges on her cushion.

"You surprised me the other day," she said, pouring the wine. She shifted in the couch, opening her body toward me.

"Am I high now?" I asked.

"No, you're not high now."

"I didn't think so. When will I be high?"

She gestured for me to take another hit, and I did, coughing hard. As I choked, I could feel Nicole's eyes burning me like the smoke in my lungs. Both were hard to take in. Sade was now playing in the background, so jazzy and cool, and when I looked at my hands, I spotted my fingers tapping to the music without my invitation. Nicole lit a candle on the coffee table, then crossed to the wall where she lowered the dimmer. When she returned, she was sitting even closer to me. She grabbed the joint from me and took another hit, putting her lips right where mine had been.

From the corner of my eye, I caught the shadow from the candle dancing on the wall. Right, left, backstep.

"How long is that shadow gonna do that?" I asked.

"Do what?"

"Flicker."

"Yeah, you're high now."

"Are you sure? Because I don't feel anything."

“Oh my God,” she laughed. She took one last hit, and leaned in toward me. Her lips just an inch from mine.

"You are going to be so much fun,” she whispered, then she blew the smoke into my mouth.

* * *

I awoke a few hours later, my brain fuzzy and hungover. The ambient light from the street shone through the window, faintly illuminating Nicole’s bedroom in dull shades of amber and blue. It was disorienting waking up this way, in someone else’s darkness, when I had grown so used to my own. I could feel Nicole’s heavy down blanket on top of me, embracing me warmly, and her impossibly soft mattress below. And her Egyptian-cotton sheets—they made mine feel like the paper you lay on top of restroom toilets. Everything here was so perfectly comfortable—everything except me. This wasn’t my life. This was someone else’s. I turned my head to the side and discovered Nicole sleeping, her mouth barely cracked open. She looked so unfamiliar this way. Not her usual confident self, but trusting and vulnerable. Asleep, she seemed like my equal. But that couldn’t be the case—I simply wouldn’t allow it. On Monday, I’d see Nicole at work again. She’d be the successful set designer sitting cross-legged on her swivel chair. And I’d still be me—the phone boy tethered to his station, dipping his toes into an imaginary pool. I lowered my feet to the floor and my body followed, dripping out of bed.

In the hallway, I found our clothes scattered about, like the cutout footprints pasted on the floor of the dance studio. I gathered my pants and achingly put them on without rattling my belt. Then I tiptoed through the darkened living room, past Nicole’s grown-up couch and coffee table. The candle had long since gone out, taking with it the shadows that danced so recklessly just a few hours earlier. As I unlocked her front door, I heard the floor creak behind me, then turned to find a figure watching from the dark. It was Nicole, shockingly naked. This time, my eyes went straight to her face and stayed there. I paused, daring her to speak first, but she said nothing. It was agonizing waiting like this, not knowing what to say or even what to think. That's the problem with dance classes. They could teach you how to move, but what I really needed to learn was how to stand still. How to just be. Finally, generously, Nicole raised her hand and casually wiggled her fingers "goodbye." I took her lead and did the same.

It was cold outside, and I walked briskly to the north toward Melrose Avenue. I hadn't yet buttoned my shirt, and the air crashed uncomfortably against my chest with every stride. After a few blocks, I suspected I was going the wrong way, and my pulse started to quicken. Even though I wasn't far, I felt lost and a little scared. My watch said three in the morning, which is why the neighborhood was completely still. There was no one on the sidewalk, and cars weren't yet driving. I was the only one going somewhere, and almost certainly in the wrong direction. At the corner, a man was standing by a street sign. His presence startled me, and I grabbed the lapel of my shirt, cinching it tighter. He was smoking a cigarette, and tugged impatiently at his dog on a leash. I picked up the pace.

"Don't follow me," I thought. It was as much a plea as it was a warning. "Don't follow *me.*"

After a few blocks, I found my car where I left it—halfway between the adult life Nicole was living and whatever it was you'd call mine. I was relieved that my key actually opened the door, half expecting the car to have changed the locks on its own, out of disapproval or disappointment. I got inside and quickly locked the door behind me, sinking into the cold seat, the frozen vinyl crackling beneath my weight as if it might suddenly shatter, sending me below.

As I pulled out of the spot, a warm cloud from my mouth fogged the windshield almost entirely. I wiped the glass with my hand, smearing it into streaks of water droplets that shattered the streetlight, making it nearly impossible to see outside. With only a hazy outline, there was not much else to guide me as I awkwardly lurched into the empty road ahead.

Merry Jewish Christmas

Growing up Jewish, I learned early on that Christmas was the greatest party I'd never be invited to. There would be no Santa coming down my chimney, no chestnuts roasting on an open fire, and no house wrapped in twinkling lights. Damn, they made Christmas tantalizing. No wonder Joseph and Mary were camped out on the neighbor's lawn. They were hoping to get a ticket inside. But sadly, the Christmas rules were very clear: No Jews allowed. The best I could do was hunker down until January 1st, when Baby New Year would shove Baby Jesus out of the way. A baby fight, that's what I was pinning my hopes on.

It's ironic that some of the most beautiful Christmas songs weren't written by Christian composers. "Chestnuts Roasting on an Open Fire," "Santa Baby," "Let It Snow," "It's the Most Wonderful Time of the Year," "Silver Bells," "White Christmas," "Rudolph the Red-Nosed Reindeer," "Walking in a Winter Wonderland" ... they were all written by Jews. When you stop to consider how that's possible, I believe it's because of this: Our version of Christmas, the one that we don't experience firsthand, is the fantasy. In Jewish Christmas, everyone loves their presents, the outside lights hang themselves, no one gets stuck in holiday traffic, and the tree never ruins your floor with sap. Christians made Christmas great, but Jews made it perfect.

As a child, I recall going to the supermarket, where "Have Yourself a Merry Little Christmas" played on the loudspeaker. Oh, that heartbreakingly beautiful song. My people were already predisposed to depression. Did we really need this as well? As I was pulled down the aisle by my mother, I watched a chef with a penchant for cookie-based architecture assemble a glorious gingerbread house that reached almost to the fluorescent bulbs that glowed so heavenly above. I was absolutely amazed. With its gumdrop-tiled roof and frosting-frosted windows, this wasn't a mere representation of Christmas, it was Christmas itself, and I wanted to live in it. If only I could shrink down to the size of a Lego man and crawl inside. I'd barricade the door by licking peppermints and sticking them together like cement blocks. Anyone who dared poke their head in would get a sharpened candy cane to the eyeball. Perhaps I'd chew the neck off a gingerbread man and leave his stiff and disfigured body propped against the licorice rain gutters, a warning to any would-be intruder that this Christmas Jew was here to stay. Good luck evicting me from a house made of bread. What government agency has jurisdiction over that?

But of course I wasn't allowed to dawdle, as my mother was in a hurry to buy ingredients for our upcoming holiday dinner. Hanukkah. She grabbed my arm and pulled me past the sugar cookies, peanut brittles, and powdered pastries that all the good Christian boys and girls got to enjoy. And where was she taking me? None other than that Jewish culinary destination known as the potato bin.

"I'm making latkes!" said my mother, as she carefully hand-selected each bland, lifeless rock that would roll downhill into our stomachs. Somewhere along the way, my ancestors had managed to take a perfectly good breakfast—the pancake—remove the delicious doughy part, and replace it with an edible tuber fried in grease. That was the problem with Jewish food. Centuries of persecution had resulted in a cuisine that was best eaten while on the run.

"And we're going to top them with applesauce!" she happily added. Applesauce—what am I, 80?

Even as my mother dragged me away from my quaint little gingerbread château, my eyes wouldn't let go—sticking to it the way a chameleon's tongue does to a fly on the wall. You could almost hear the ligaments in my eyeballs straining to remain in contact with it.

"Can gingerbread houses be a Hanukkah thing, too?" I asked my mother, hopefully.

The poor woman couldn't find the words to let me down gently. So, instead, she took the opposite path. "You don't want that Christmas shit. It's all diabetes." And we continued on our way.

I can't blame her for shielding me from all the Christmas temptation. Parents want to give their kids everything, and this was definitely something she couldn't, despite all my pleading. Frosty the Snowman standing at the checkout aisle wasn't making things easier. With his corncob pipe and eyes of coal, he was both scrappy and delightful. What religion wouldn't want to claim him as their own?

"Is Frosty Christian?" I asked my mother.

"Are you kidding me?" she said. "He probably drives a Camaro." And she went back to bowling dinner potatoes down the cashier's conveyor belt.

To be honest, this whole Hanukkah thing needed a lot of rethinking. Part of the problem is that you couldn't hype its arrival because it never fell on the same date. The Jewish calendar is lunisolar. Sometimes Hanukkah would land near Christmas. Other times, it came shockingly early.

"Hey, did you know Hanukkah falls on November 30th this year?"

"November? Oh, for fuck's sake."

And the lore behind Hanukkah needed work, too. It was all about lamp oil that was supposed to last only one day, but by some miracle, burned for eight days. Is that really a miracle, or is it just good fuel economy? When I was little, we had a container of orange juice that lasted two full weeks. Every morning I'd pour myself a glass, and the next day—like a magic trick—the carton somehow contained more juice than yesterday. I couldn't believe it! But after two weeks, I finally discovered why my Tropicana was as thin as a urine sample—my mother was just cutting it with water. That's not a miracle—that's a crime. But talking snowmen and flying reindeer ... now that was a miracle!

The Christian kids at school used to mock us. They knew their ancestors had built a better holiday, and they weren't afraid to shove it in our faces. Inevitably, some Jewish kid would lash out, "*We're* the ones who feel bad for *you*. We have eight days of presents, and you only have one!"

But that was bullshit. Everyone knew seven of those days were for socks or pencils or soap-on-a-rope. Who did this schmuck think he was kidding? He's trying to pass off Hanukkah ... or "Chanukah" ... as the greatest holiday ever, and we couldn't even agree on the spelling. As it stood, I'd have to admire the joy of Christmas from afar. Until one eve, one foggy Christmas Eve, when I managed to experience Christmas as an insider.

It happened while on vacation in Amish country, in Pennsylvania. It was my father's idea to take us there, instead of someplace good, like Disney World. As we drove through the farmland, passing simple wooden barns and horse-drawn buggies, my father noted how life in the Amish country was about hard work, sacrifice, and living without technology. This jab wasn't lost on me, as I had been constantly nagging him to buy me an Atari. To the ignorant or desirably young, Atari was an early video-game console. In its most popular game, you could hit a square that was supposed to be a ball against a rectangle that was supposed to be a paddle. In real life, this would've been dreadfully boring, but plug it into a TV and my generation was hooked. My father didn't like me hounding him for one, and now I was forced to learn a lesson in deprivation.

"See that Amish man plowing the field? You can't even take a picture of him."

"Is it because you won't buy me a camera?" I said.

"It's because his religion forbids it! And don't be a wiseass."

We spent Christmas Eve at a nearby resort that was *the* vacation spot ... in 1958. Once upscale and chic, the hotel had fallen into disrepair. Wallpaper weeped off the walls in sorrow, and the carpeting, thin and sticky, had its own emotional issues. Yes, a fire roared in the lobby, but I can only imagine it was fueled by a mountain of state-issued safety violations. Fortunately, whatever money they saved in sprinkler upgrades that could potentially save our lives was spent on Christmas decorations that brought wonder to my Hebrew eyes. Flecks of silver and gold were splayed everywhere, and they had a name for it: tinsel. I learned other words too. The aging pianist in the lobby sang of mythical creatures that were half reptile and half bird, called "turtledoves." They sounded slow and peaceful, and I dreamed of keeping one in a tank. There was a log called a "yule," and in a bowl there was a "nog." It was magical.

On Christmas morning, we awoke to find fresh snowfall on the ground, just like the movies promised. I could've done a happy little dance in my feet-y pajamas, were I not so worried about my penis flopping out of the crotch fold. My sister and I quickly got dressed and raced downstairs to the Christmas tree, silently shouting, "Santa! Santa!" And there, handing out presents to a hoard of waiting children, was the big man himself—Jolly Saint Nick.

"Go get one," urged my mother.

"But we're Jewish!"

"He doesn't know that. He's probably drunk. Pick a big one."

I was so conflicted. Wasn't I supposed to be proud of my heritage? Isn't that why my parents sent me to Hebrew school every Sunday? Or was that just punishment for something?

"You go first," I said to my sister, and she was gone in a flash—leaving the napkin she used to hold her sugar cookies still hovering in the air, the way they do in cartoons. Apparently, she didn't have the same reservations I did about deceiving transients dressed as fictional deities.

My mother nudged me to keep up with her. "Go on, before they're all gone."

I approached, just as Santa was being handed a fresh stack of presents from one of his elves, who I now recognized as our busboy from last night's dinner. I said nothing, though. We were both keeping secrets.

Admittedly, I took pleasure in receiving a present from Santa Claus, and the fact that I might be depriving a deserving Christian child just because he was late getting to the lobby didn't bother me in the slightest. Did that make me a bad person, or had I already crossed that threshold when I told Santa my name was Timmy?

I rushed to a quiet part of the lobby to unwrap my Christmas bounty. I was certain mine contained the perfect toy—probably that Atari my father wouldn't get me. The moment before unwrapping any gift is always special, because that's when the present is at its highest potential. It could be anything you wanted it to be. I suppose the same could be said about a Jewish child about to experience Christmas for the first time. Just imagine.

I ravenously tore off the paper that was standing between me and pure Christmas joy. "Fa-la-la-la-la," sang my heart with each rip. And now imagine my disappointment when I discovered what lay beneath. It was a bargain-rack board game that the hotel picked up at the thrift store. Santa knew all along who I was, and he knifed me right in the Jewish gut. I had betrayed my heritage by pretending to be Christian, and for what? A lousy board game.

"What do you think?" said my mother, as I fell against the wall, clutching my stomach, straining for my final words.

"I think ... this sucks."

"I told you to pick a big one," she said, sipping the hot cocoa I asked her to hold but not drink.

I should've tossed that game right in the garbage, but I couldn't. It was my sole Christmas present. It had to be good—it just had to be. If I hung on to it long enough, maybe it would transform itself. So I packed it into the back of our Volvo and brought it home with me, where it taunted me from the bottom of my shelf for several years. Not once did I play with it. And although I don't recall the exact name of this board game, for the sake of things, let's just call it Abject Disappointment, by Parker Brothers.

And so my desire to celebrate Christmas was completely quashed. It only resurfaced years later, when my daughters were little. My mother-in-law was trying to convince me to let my children celebrate it.

"It's an American holiday," she insisted. "It's not religious anymore."

"Not religious? It's got the word 'Christ' in it, and the first three letters of 'mass.' I'd say their branding is spot-on."

Americans may have been the first to commercialize Christmas, but by no means was it an American holiday. It's Christian through and through. The kicker is, my mother-in-law is Jewish. She, like so many other Jews I knew, had the same latent urge to get in on the Christmas spirit. Maybe her dream wasn't as grandiose as squatting inside a gingerbread house, but she had visions nonetheless. This was a trend that had been sweeping my people for some time: Jews buying Christmas trees and calling them "Hanukkah bushes." But not me. I had crossed that bridge once before, and it's as brittle as the peanuts it's paved with.

"Look, Bonnie," I said. "I know Hanukkah isn't quite Christmas, but we have to make the best out of a bad situation. Instead of making my daughters feel like they're missing out, let's take a different path. Let's teach them to mock the Christians for commercializing what should be a sacred holiday, even though that's exactly what we'd do in their situation." My words held no sway over her.

"You're the Jew who stole Christmas," she scoffed, but she was wrong. I had tried to steal Christmas, but failed.

To this day, Christmas morning holds an unnerving stillness for me. When most of the population is inside unwrapping presents and spreading good cheer, we Jews wander the vacant city just like Joseph and Mary, searching for a destination that will take us in. Usually, it's a Chinese restaurant. So that's what Cynthia and I did with our daughters when we pulled open the door to Szechuan Dragon.

It's strange to have a restaurant almost entirely to yourself.

Even if you're with someone, there's a loneliness to it. A lack of belonging. At least that's how I felt when our moo shu vegetables arrived. We sat at a window table, our hands resting on the cold glass surface, staring outside, where not even a mouse was stirring. Closer to the door was an older couple who had grappled with a similar feeling, but ordered the noodles instead. For a moment, the woman and I made eye contact.

On any other day, we may have both looked away. But this was Christmas. Even though we were strangers, I think we wanted to share a feeling of connection. Or at least acknowledge our sense of isolation. She gave me a smile that said, "Eh, whaddaya gonna do?" I shrugged and dipped my egg roll in duck sauce. What else could be done?

When our meal was over, I ordered a serving of mooncake. Not much, just a little sweetness to help enjoy the day. As I ushered my family out the door, I set it down at the woman's table.

"Merry Jewish Christmas," I said.

"Merry Jewish Christmas to you too."

Melrose Last Place

Dave was my first roommate out of college, and I moved in without even knowing him. He was just the brother of a girl I knew in high school. He made a living working in television, which is what I aspired to do, and she said he'd be glad to offer me advice. He was only a few years older than me, but the first time I called, I was worried he might be too important to talk to me. Luckily, he didn't pick up on the first ring, which gave me time to rehearse saying my name out loud. I needed it. The first two times, "Michael" came out sounding like "My Gull." My Gull Jamin, bird collector.

On the third ring, Dave picked up with a simple but effective hello. I was charmed by the manner in which a person of his stature answered the phone. No assistant or answering service. He did it himself. So humble.

I soon learned that he wasn't exactly Spielberg. In fact, he had spent the last few years producing schlocky, low-budget syndicated programming. Shows about deadbeats running from the law, that kind of thing. But still ... Hollywood!

And at the end of our conversation, he casually mentioned

that he lived right off Melrose Avenue and was looking for a new roommate.

"Melrose? As in *Melrose Place*?"

At that time, *Melrose Place* was one of the biggest shows on television. It was a night-time soap opera that followed the exciting lives of several incredibly attractive twentysomethings living in a charming Spanish-style apartment complex in Los Angeles. The characters included a budding fashion designer, a receptionist, a gay social worker, a physician and his psychotic wife, and most importantly, an aspiring screenwriter. Just like me. Even though the writer was struggling, his plight was exciting. Sure, he had setbacks, but they were only temporary. An episode or two later, he'd be having sex with someone else's wife, who was even hotter.

"Yep," responded Dave. "Just like the show *Melrose Place.*"

That was all I needed to hear.

"I'll be there in five days." Then I hung up before Dave could change his mind.

For a kid who wanted to be a TV writer, the idea of moving to the real address of a fictional television show was very exciting. The people I'd meet. The jobs I'd take. I packed all my belongings into my car, told my mother I loved her, then headed west to start my life. It was a plan that felt impetuous and dramatic, like the inciting incident on an episode of *Melrose Place.* But when I finally arrived in Hollywood and pulled up to Dave's apartment building, I did a double take. I didn't think his apartment would be exactly like the one on *Melrose Place*, but there wasn't even a semblance. Where were the young starlets sunbathing by the pool in the courtyard? Where was the pool? Where was the courtyard, for God's sake?

There was a metal security gate at the front entrance that looked like something you might find at a correctional facility.

The gate must've been for appearances only, as no robber in the world would've looked at this building and thought, "I want what's in there." I'd later discover that the residents didn't want what was in there, either. Most moved out the minute they could afford it. The previous tenants of our unit didn't even leave a change of address. Their mail just piled up in our mailbox, as if living there was a mistake they didn't want to be reminded of.

Moments after carrying my first bag into Dave's apartment, I met Dave's current roommate, Erica. She was the one whose lease I was taking over. Even though we'd be living under the same roof for only a few days, I saw her as my first potential friend in the real world. Erica, unfortunately, saw things differently. To her, I wasn't a friend—I was the asshole crashing on her couch. When I introduced myself, she greeted me with a scowl. Under different circumstances, I probably would've said something hurtful back to her. The low road, that's the one I usually travel on. You hurt me, I hurt you harder. But this was different. I was grateful to be here. I was going to make it work.

Dave, on the other hand, couldn't have been more gracious. He greeted me with a hug and took me in. As a television producer, his job was to come up with ideas, an exercise which he loved even when he wasn't on the clock. Every problem had 10 potential solutions, and it was just a matter of time before he figured out my problem—which was how to break into Hollywood. His confidence was so endearing, I was willing to overlook the fact that he himself hadn't worked in months.

On my second day of living in Los Angeles, Dave offered to take me to Ralphs.

"That sounds great! Thank you!" I hopped into his car without even asking who Ralph was. Was he a friend of his? Was he a headhunter who'd help me find work? It didn't really matter, though, because I was building my network, and that was the important thing. I'd soon learn that Ralphs was our regional supermarket chain. Not quite what I was hoping, but still, it's good to have contacts in Breads and Crackers.

"Do you get the sense that Erica doesn't want me here?" I asked as we grabbed a shopping cart.

"Yes."

Erica, it turns out, was also an aspiring sitcom writer. At first, I thought this would be great for me. We could bond over that, maybe even help each other out. But Dave explained that would never be the case. Ever. Get it out of your head. Put it in the toilet. Flush it twice. To Erica, I was the competition—someone trying to steal her dream. *Melrose Place* already had one aspiring screenwriter, and there wasn't room for two. I could be the gay social worker or the psychotic wife, but you don't want to rush into either of those choices. Being young, I didn't realize that Erica's animosity was her problem, not mine. So I became the guy who apologized. "Sorry for being in your way." "Sorry for using the bathroom." "Sorry I exist."

"Help yourself to doughnuts in the kitchen," I offered to her one day. I bought them from Ralph as a goodwill gesture.

"That sounds supe," answered Erica, dismissively, before walking away. "Supe" was short for "super." She didn't even have the decency to give me the *r*.

When Erica finally moved out, I took over her bedroom, and I could see why she was so surly. The room wasn't much bigger than a prison cell, and when the wind blew, the hanging vinyl blinds clacked together like an inmate rattling the bars. The mirrored sliding doors of the closet were supposed to make the room seem more spacious, but it had the opposite effect. Seeing my reflection all day made the space feel more crowded—like I shared my cell with someone guilty of the same crime. Guilty of having a dream. I'd catch him looking at me then bark back, "What's *your* problem, sweetheart?"

Over the next few weeks, Dave laid out a plan for me to break into Hollywood as a production assistant. Cold phone calls followed up by letters, all of it tracked on a spreadsheet. As simple as it was, none of this was obvious to me, and it made this crazy goal of mine feel attainable. Until it didn't. Despite sending out letters day after day, month after month, all my solicitations were met with silence. I couldn't even get a no from people. Even Erica was kind enough to give me a no. Was there something wrong with my approach? Did I sound too needy?

"Do I sound too needy, Dave?"

"No."

Maybe I sounded too confident.

"Do I sound too confident, Dave?"

"You're asking me if you sound too confident?"

One morning, I decided to go for a run. It was a good idea to escape the confines of my cell. A little time away from my reflection would do us both good. Dave and I lived at the corner of Melrose Avenue, but during this run, I discovered a street named Melrose Place. This was the actual name of the TV show, and it was only a few hundred yards away. I ran down it, but it was little more than an alley with a handful of antique shops. No hot models lounging poolside. I checked. Twice.

I brought this up with Dave, who wasn't really sure what to do with my complaint. It was like saying, "Hey, did you know the tooth fairy isn't real?"

Dave suggested that, from now on, I run in the opposite direction—away from my dream. But running east on Melrose, toward the commercial district, didn't feel right to me. I moved here from the East. New York. On some small level, running in that direction felt like I was running home in defeat. Dave assured me that wasn't the case, and once again, I thanked him for his guidance.

Melrose was famous for its quirky storefronts that catered mostly to teenagers. Bongs, novelties, electronics ... anything that might break within five minutes of buying. Sandwiched between a magazine stand and a sneaker store was a low-rent, assisted-living home—a not-so-subtle reminder to the youth that, eventually, they would break, too.

While running past it, I heard an elderly woman yell from her ground-floor balcony, "Stop!" And because I desperately needed guidance, I did.

"Take this across the street and buy me a Coke," she said, waving two dollars at me.

"Excuse me?"

She pointed to Johnny Rockets, a burger place opposite us. "And bring me a straw."

"I'm in the middle of running."

"Good. You'll be fast."

I was stunned. Why, in a million years, did she think I would stop everything for her? Especially given how rude she was. Was the word "schmuck" written on my forehead?

"Okay," I replied, confirming that the word "schmuck" was, indeed, written on my forehead.

"Don't steal it," she warned as she handed me the cash. Steal it? I didn't even want it!

I took her money across the street to Johnny Rockets, watching myself go, as if having an out-of-body experience. Someone else might chalk my gesture up as a good deed, but even in the moment, I knew I wasn't doing this for her—I was doing it for me. I was just so lonely. After months of solitude in my bedroom, sending out messages in bottles, I just wanted someone to acknowledge my existence. Someone to confirm that I was on the same planet as everyone else.

I returned to her, holding a soda, a straw, and a few coins. The old woman didn't thank me, but she did tell me to "keep the change." I looked at the money in my hand. It couldn't have been more than eight cents.

"These are running shorts," I said. "They don't have pockets."

I loitered for a moment, hoping she might offer me not a few pennies but something way more valuable. Something that would keep me glued together for another day. I placed my foot on the curb to re-tie my shoelace. I thought stalling like this might give her the time she needed, but instead she simply pulled the paper from the straw with her teeth, yanking it like the pin from a hand grenade.

My mind went to a memory that comes to me every now and then. I was a little boy at summer camp in suburban New York. Our group was hiking deep into the woods, crunching on fallen leaves and pushing through ferns and saplings. I was nervous about venturing from home, and every few minutes, I glanced back, watching the building that we came from grow smaller and smaller.

"We're exploring!" shouted one of the campers as he jumped across a small stream. Others quickly followed, but when it was my turn to jump, I hesitated. It wasn't so much the crossing of it that scared me as it was the realization that, if I did, I'd be on the other side. And that seemed too far.

I turned around once again, but the building had disappeared under the ridge, and now I felt lost. Quietly, tears started rolling down my face. For some reason, without seeing that building, I could no longer feel my parents' love. There was no one to comfort me, and I was alone. Embarrassed, I did my best to hide my tears. But then I felt a hand on my shoulder. It belonged to a teenage girl—a counselor from one of the other groups. She had no reason to look after me, but somehow she found me. She kneeled down and put her arms around me.

"Your eyes are so pretty when you cry," she said.

That's all she had to say, really. Then she smiled, took my hand, and helped me along the way. I think that's what I was hoping to get from this old woman on Melrose Avenue. Just a moment of kindness. But she said nothing, and just sipped on her soda. I stopped running and walked the rest of the way back to my apartment.

It was on a hot October morning, four months after moving to Hollywood, that I got my first job interview. It didn't come from any of the cover letters I sent out—those were all dead ends. It came from a friend of Dave's, who was a working sitcom writer. She heard that her agent was looking for a new assistant and sent me the lead. It was such a gracious thing for her to do, and I thanked her profusely, promising that if I got the job I would not let her down.

The agent, I'll change her name to "Julie" because her real name still makes me flinch like my nipples are about to be shocked with a car battery, worked at a large talent agency. Ordinarily, outsiders can't be hired to be an agent's assistant. Those opportunities fall to young graduates who've earned the right to a desk job, only after spending a year in the mail room. The fact that Julie was willing to meet me, despite not having the bona fides of knowing how to deliver an envelope, was a giant coup.

Julie was a petite woman, maybe 35 years old, very smart, and built for the job. I say "built" because the manufacturer never installed her heart. When I interviewed, I don't think she was terribly impressed by me. In fact, she barely asked me any questions. I think she offered me the job simply because she didn't want to talk to more people like me.

Dave was thrilled when he heard the news, and he took me out for Thai food to celebrate. While he was heaping *pad see ew* onto my plate, I felt guilty for not sharing his enthusiasm. Julie made me uncomfortable. It was the way she sized me up, not like I was a person but a commodity. Like a pallet of mangoes being offloaded from a steamship. Julie didn't seem like the kind of person who would take my hand and help me across a stream. She seemed like someone who would push me into the water. Besides, did I really want to work in a talent agency? I was hoping to find a job working on a television show, something closer to the action, but Dave insisted this was the next best thing. Agencies are the hub of the entertainment business. It's where talent meets commerce, and I'd be exposed to both sides of it. I could read as many scripts as I wanted, maybe make it onto a set once in a while, and over time, learn about other opportunities. The only downside was that I was expected to wear a suit and tie to work every day. But so did lots of other people. Dave was right. I resolved to start my first big-boy job with an attitude of positivity.

I showed up to my first day of training at eight A.M. Despite being one of the oldest, most prestigious agencies in Beverly Hills, the building itself didn't feel venerated. It wasn't impressive or stately in the least. It was just your average, nondescript office building—like it was made by the same builders who did my apartment. If the agents wanted a sense of superiority, they couldn't derive it from the architecture. They'd have to get it someplace else.

Tamiko, the woman I'd be replacing, met me in the lobby. She was about my age, but she carried herself differently. This was where all the Hollywood power brokers were, so I walked cautiously, as if I were on a tightrope. Not Tamiko, though. She walked completely unafraid. At first, I interpreted this to mean she was confident and self-assured. I later came to realize it wasn't about that. As she escorted me to her workstation, we passed row after row of assistants. Most of them looked exhausted, like they hadn't slept in years. They were seated at desks surrounded on three sides by padded fabric walls, where memos were thumbtacked. They were cushy, but not quite sturdy enough to bounce off, like a real padded cell. Some were people like me, using this job as a stepping stone to something more creative. They looked like shelter animals, with their vacant eyes screaming, "Take me home!" Others looked cocky and arrogant, future agents, for sure. None of them looked human.

Tamiko was pleasant enough, but when she spoke, she sounded off. Her audio track didn't quite sync up with her video track. When I asked her how to work the phones, she told me about the supply closet. And when I asked her about the supply closet, she told me how to validate guest parking. If she were a television set, you would've slapped her on the head.

I quickly realized that Tamiko was completely disassociated from reality. Instead of being miserably tethered to the tiny cubicle sitting outside Julie's office, Tamiko was somewhere else. Maybe lounging on a beach. Or maybe she was standing inside a hangman's noose, eager to have the floor pulled away. Either would've been more enjoyable than being here. I was only getting a taste of this workplace, and it wasn't my flavor. But the main course arrived an hour later, when Julie walked in.

"Where's my *Hollywood Reporter*?" she shouted, and I jumped, as if someone had just fired a starter's pistol in my ear.

Tamiko pulled a magazine out of Julie's mail bin and handed it to her. The bin was only a foot away from Julie. She could've easily taken it herself, but that wasn't her style. She needed to summon it.

"Welcome," she said to me, in a tone that wasn't welcoming at all, and I smiled in fear.

"You have nothing to worry about, Julie. Michael's the perfect replacement," said Tamiko, "He's absolutely perfect!" I was struck by how brazen her lie was. I had done nothing to suggest I would be good at this job. I even struggled filling in my time card. But that wasn't important to Tamiko. All she cared about was selling me to Julie, so that someone—anyone—would take her place.

As the morning progressed, Julie barked out orders, which Tamiko would interpret for me. There was so much to remember, and I quickly became overwhelmed.

"Here's how to take notes when you listen in on Julie's phone calls."

"I have to listen in on Julie's phone calls?"

"And here's how to keep Julie's phone log."

"I have to keep Julie's phone log?"

"And here's how to keep Julie's calendar. And here's how Julie likes to have her calls placed."

It seemed Tamiko's entire job was to do Julie's job. And on top of this, she had to do it while writing cover letters, mailing out scripts, and fetching coffee. It was air-traffic control, only in Julie's mind, the stakes were much higher. A plane that dropped out of the sky would be sad. But a plain macchiato that dropped to the floor would be ... well, let's not even go there.

"Why haven't I read this script yet?" Julie barked from her desk.

"I left a copy in your bag for you to read over the weekend."

"Then why didn't I read it!!!"

"It was one of the entries I put on your to-do list."

"Then why didn't I read my to-do list?"

Are you fucking kidding me? Is this what Hollywood is like? I looked at poor Tamiko, certain that I would have to walk her back from a nervous breakdown, but she didn't seem fazed or worried at all. She had not a care in the world. She was completely checked out, and her bags were waiting at the curb. "All aboard to outer space!"

"Where the hell are my car keys!" shouted Julie. "They were in my hand a minute ago!"

"Oh God, now we have to find her keys?"

"Do you like cinnamon rolls?" asked Tamiko, looking my way. "You're gonna love the cinnamon rolls here."

"Cinnamon rolls?! Where are you, Tamiko? Where have you gone?"

All the while, the notepad that I was frantically writing notes on was filling up quickly. Page after page, there was so much to remember that my handwriting couldn't keep up. It was no longer legible, and I knew I wouldn't be able to interpret anything when I needed it most. And the phones were ringing, and more mail was coming in, and the scripts were piling up, and Julie was still barking orders ...

"Wednesday is my last day," said Tamiko, licking cinnamon roll from her fingertips. I was so overwhelmed by everything around me that it appeared out of nowhere, like a magic trick.

"But that's in two days. You can't leave me alone, Tamiko. I'm not ready."

"Oh, you'll be fine. I'll introduce you to Derek." Now she was eating French-bread pizza and washing it down with a Diet Coke. Where the hell did that come from?!

Tamiko led me down the hall to a nearby cubicle, while I scribbled "Derek" on my notepad. Julie's phone began to ring.

"Shouldn't we pick up the—" But Tamiko was now skipping through the aisle, which was lined with tulips and heroin.

"Derek, this is Michael. He's Julie's new assistant." Derek grunted at me, barely raising his eyes from his computer screen. With his slicked-back hair and Winchester dress shirt, he was a future agent, for sure—possibly a partner. He had a handmade sign tacked to the wall of his cubicle that read: ICM SUCKS. "ICM" was the name of a rival talent agency, and I was surprised he felt so much antipathy toward it, when this place was the waterslide that led to hell. How could ICM suck any harder than here? Did the ICM agents throw darts at your neck? And if they killed you, would that be considered an act of cruelty or mercy? I instantly disliked Derek.

"So, what's next for you?" asked Derek to Tamiko. He was chewing on the back of a pen, and I was summoning my powers of psychokinesis to make it explode in his mouth.

"Blow up, you shitty Bic pen! Blow up!"

"Oh, I don't know. I don't even care!" she laughed. Honestly, Tamiko could not have been happier.

My eyes went to my notepad, where the name "Derek" had been scrawled for some reason. Did I write this? Who's Derek?

"Why is my phone ringing?!" shouted Julie from down the hall. Oh, crap, Julie's phone is ringing! It's ringing! I quickly scampered back to Tamiko's desk, gripping my notepad for dear life.

"No one is answering!" Now I was actually running. Not walking fast, but sprinting toward more humiliation. Please, Julie, is there anything else you can do to make me feel worse about myself? Surely you can offer me something!

"I need a loser to pick up my phone!" Perfect, thank you.

"I got it!" I screamed in victory, diving into Tamiko's chair, almost tipping it over, while grabbing the receiver.

"Julie Farber's office, please hold." I exhaled. Thank God the day was almost over. The clock on the wall read 9:52 A.M.

* * *

"I know it's bad, but you'll get used to it." This was Dave the next morning, trying to give me the courage to get out of bed. I was gripping the covers under my neck, like a chin-up bar. My first day of work in the real world was so sobering. I thought I could do anything if I tried hard enough, but clearly not this. It just wasn't in my temperament, and the thought of returning to that World War I foxhole located at the corner of Indignity and Degradation put a knot in my stomach. It's amazing how quickly things change. Twenty-four hours ago, I saw my bedroom as a prison cell. Now it was a safe room. I didn't want to leave—ever again, for any reason. But I had no choice.

I arrived at work, 10 minutes early, resolved that if I just gave a little more of myself, 110 percent instead of a mere 100 percent, I might be okay. I could stick it out for a year or so, then use this opportunity as the springboard to better things. I trudged to my desk, and there, to my horror, was Tamiko, happily organizing paperwork while sipping from a coffee cup tall enough for its own elevator.

"You're here early," I said in complete disbelief.

"Yeah, I thought I'd help catch you up."

"Catch up? You mean I'm behind?"

"A little bit. I did most of it last night after you left."

"Wait a minute. I worked until 10 last night. You stayed later?!"

"Only a hour."

"Only an hour?! I worked 14 hours yesterday."

My heart fell into my loafers, which were teetering on the precipice of a volcano. In comparison to this place, diving in would've felt cool and refreshing.

I spent my lunch break at the desk, working. I was transcribing my barely legible notes so that I could understand them when Tamiko was gone. She was dumping a bag of microwave popcorn into a bowl for Julie. I don't know why she bothered, when Julie could've easily popped it with her Godzilla breath. Anyway, that's when Tamiko handed me the headset to her phone.

"It's yours now," she said, as if a curse had been lifted from her and placed on me. I put it on, the earphones still warm from brain melt. I hated wearing them, but they did, however, muffle the outside noise, and that gave me some calm. I relished the silence, and it must've been this small fragment of joy that provoked the phones to light up, quashing it for good.

"Julie Farber's office, please hold ... Julie Farber's office, please hold ... Julie Farber's office, please hold ... "

I had four calls on hold, and I yelled out the names of each one to Julie.

"Which one's my cleaning lady?" she barked.

"Line three."

I think. How was I supposed to know who her cleaning lady was?

Julie picked up her phone, and through the glass window that separated me from her, I could see her face grow livid. She gestured at me frantically without actually saying anything—just flailing her arms, as if a cloud of bees was attacking her. Finally, she hung up the phone and stormed to my desk.

"That wasn't my cleaning lady!"

"I'm sorry, I must've gotten confused."

"Confused?! That was a client I didn't want to talk to!" Julie was now crimson with rage, her face as red as her nails, which were as red as her shoes, which were as red as her dress. I braced for what came next.

"Michael!" she shouted. "Does everyone in the world think you're a complete fucking idiot?!"

The entire office froze, silently watching Julie's rage as it crashed over my head like a wave, drenching me with failure. It dripped down my face, soaking my shirt and shoes. It was an ostentatious display of humiliation, and everyone got to witness it. Even Tamiko saw it, all the way from the fourth ring of Saturn.

"Why don't you take a little break," Tamiko whispered to me. I nodded and slinked to the courtyard, where a few assistants were smoking cigarettes to hasten their deaths. Alone, I considered what I wanted my future to look like. Not my distant future—my five-minutes-from-now future. I couldn't see a world where I put up with this pitiful existence one second longer. How was I going to survive this nightmare? A nightmare that I was supposed to use to chase a dream. I returned to Tamiko's desk.

"Feeling better now?" she asked, fearful of hearing the wrong answer. I said nothing, and continued into Julie's office, where I opened her door without knocking and helped myself to the seat opposite her desk. It was a bold move, considering the window behind her was still fogged with steam coming from her head. I imagined tracing my finger in it, rubbing, "I'm sorry." The thought of it made my stomach turn. Then I imagined tracing, "Fuck this." That felt better.

"I don't think this is the right place for me." I said it calmly, even though my heart was still pounding.

"Yes, I would have to fucking agree."

I crossed to the door, wondering how I'd break the news to everyone who believed in me. This was my first job in the real world, and I failed. And after only two days. My parents, Dave, Dave's friend who got me the job, my needy reflection in the closet mirror ... there were a lot of people who were about to see me in a new light, and it wouldn't be flattering. Tamiko took the news especially hard. The candle of hope that was burning behind her eyes blew suddenly out, leaving behind just a smoldering wick. Its smoke wafted into the ethers, and she grasped at it, desperate to hitch a ride out. Poor Tamiko, so close to freedom.

I was too young to understand why Julie made me feel like an object and not a person. It would take years before I realized that being a Hollywood agent almost requires it. Agents connect artists with buyers, but like all middlemen, they don't actually produce anything. Their job is to know as many people as possible, and in order to be really successful, they have to traffic in those people. They have to treat them like a commodity, like a pallet of mangoes. When a client outlives their usefulness, they're tossed aside to make room for someone with more value. It has to happen that way. They have to forget that people are human beings—human beings that sometimes feel scared and need help crossing a stream.

But of course, I didn't know this back then. I was just a young man who naïvely thought breaking into Hollywood was going to be fun and exciting, like a night-time soap opera. I'd make friendships easily, like I had in college. And if I ever felt lonely, a stranger might sense that and feel compelled to be kind.

In other words, just a complete fucking idiot.

No One Speaks to Master Huang

The last words my father said to me before I moved to California were "Don't go California on me." He meant it as a joke, but like all jokes, there was a hint of judgment beneath it, and it made me think he didn't support my decision. In his mind, California was a refuge for New Age freaks who, at the blessing of liberal lawmakers in Sacramento, had turned the part of their brain responsible for reason into an open-air drum circle. Were someone to ask if they had rocks for brains, my father would say, "Not quite. Crystals." I get where he was coming from. My dad made his living in the corporate world. He worked with numbers on spreadsheets, which made decisions quantifiable, and considering it provided his family with a pretty good lifestyle, I had no reason to doubt him. And because he operated in the world of facts, it was therefore easy to think that his opinions were also facts.

"Always drink your coffee black," I remember him telling me as a child while we were having breakfast at our local diner. "That way you taste the bean, and not the sweetener."

He said this quietly, almost whispering, which was what he

did whenever conveying something of import. It was a trick he learned from a dog-training book written by monks in upstate New York, and he also applied it to his children.

"You'll see people put milk or even sugar in their coffee," he continued, "But that doesn't make it right." He took a long sip, savoring every note like the philharmonic was playing Mozart in his mouth. Years later, when I moved to California, not only did I always drink my coffee black, I hadn't even tried it any other way.

He had other rules, like "Only eat kosher hot dogs." The ingredients in hot dogs are famously disgusting. Rat shit, bird beaks—government certifications allow for acceptable levels of it. But if the hot dog was kosher, at least you could be assured it wasn't made from pork. So that's how I grew up—closed-minded, but with a stomach free of pig dick.

As is often the case, it was desperation that finally forced me to open my mind a little. It happened a few years ago in the middle of the night, when my brain woke me up with a matter so urgent, it couldn't possibly wait until morning.

"What is it?" I asked myself. "What am I worried about?" But my mind was a blank. Usually I worry about deadlines, tests, bills, and jobs. But I had finally arrived at a place in my life where things seemed fine. So what was I struggling with?

My insomnia went on for a few weeks, and it quickly turned me into the worst version of myself. Everything became an irritant, and I just couldn't keep my discomfort a secret. The world needed to know how I was suffering. During one of my outbursts, which must've seemed completely unprovoked, I overheard my mother-in-law ask Cynthia, "Do you think Michael's on the spectrum?" At first I was offended that she thought I was autistic, but after a moment's consideration, I realized, "Yeah, that could be."

In truth, my natural resting state, even when I'm well rested, isn't very tolerant. A therapist once had me take a long questionnaire, and after tallying the results, diagnosed me as a "highly sensitive person." It sounded like a compliment. Like I might burst into tears at the thought of an injured sparrow.

"No, that's not what 'highly sensitive' means," he corrected me. "It means everything bothers you a lot." It was just a clinical way of saying I could be an asshole. My first thought was, "Who gives a shit what you think, prick!"

I have a hard time tolerating things that others enjoy—like parties or concerts. Too many people, too much noise, too much to see. It would be easy if that stimulation just passed through me, but that's not how it works. It has to go into my brain, where it's assigned a judgment, then directed to a queue for further classification. There's a queue for derision, a queue for envy, and a queue for empathy. There's no one manning that line, so if you're in a hurry for empathy, I recommend going somewhere else.

I guess I could've turned to a physician for sleeping pills, but that didn't appeal to me. It didn't feel like a medical problem, like strep throat or pink eye. It's just sleep. Even babies can do it. I just needed a factory reset, like when your iPhone freaks out.

Cynthia, who is so much a Californian that it's listed as her blood type, suggested I try something completely out of the box.

"You're going to say no to this," she said while I was nursing a cup of black coffee that my father would've approved of, "but please, just do it for me." That's a bullshit trick she's been pulling for years to try to make me a better person, because she knows there's nothing I wouldn't do for her. It's manipulative is what it is. It's why I pop gelcaps full of oregano oil when I have a cold. Or why I keep magic crystals next to my computer. I don't think they help with my creativity, but they're not making things worse, so they can stay.

"I've heard of a man that can help with your insomnia," she said. I was already rolling my eyes. It was the vagueness of her description that irritated me. "I've heard of a man." It made him sound like a myth—a lost soul wandering the planet. An ancient sorcerer, perhaps.

"He's not an ancient sorcerer," she scoffed.

"Uh-huh. So what's his name?"

"Master Huang."

Please, that's exactly the name of an ancient sorcerer. It would say so on the front cover of his book of spells. "If lost, please return to Master Huang. Fourth century B.C." I shot her a disdainful look that said everything. There was no subtlety or nuance in the judgment that came out of my eyes, but I opened my mouth just to be 100 percent clear.

"I need sleep, not magic squeezed out of a ruby."

"You don't know everything," she said. "He does Qigong. It manipulates your life force. It's proven."

"It's proven?"

"Not scientifically. But in other ways." Cynthia is like that. She'll make a bold statement, but when you call her on it, she'll completely back down. Not me. When I'm talking bullshit, I dig my heels in.

"Well, you can get that thought out of your mind, because I'm never, ever going to see Master Huang!"

* * *

The drive to Master Huang's office took an hour and a half. I thought it would be longer, considering I expected to find him perched on top of a volcano. Two more weeks of insomnia made me change my mind, but there was also something deeper at play. I was raised to believe that anything was possible as long as I worked hard. And that turned out well for me. I was accepted into an Ivy League college, and later, landed my dream job as a sitcom writer. After I was hired on my first show, I can remember walking through the airport thinking, "I'm a writer on a hit TV show watched by millions of people. Everyone here wants my job." It's a very high level of delusion, and I have to say, it feels wonderful. But a few years later, something shifted. I learned that some relationships don't work, some careers have setbacks, and some desires are simply outside my power. In short, I had learned humility.

I think that's what makes some people turn to religion. Or even drugs. It's the realization that control over your own life is just an illusion. Things may have gone your way a few times, but you never truly had control, and you never will have control. So to get what you want, you appeal to a higher force. A god, an energy, a pill, whatever. So part of my decision to seek help from the great Master Huang was that I was willing to accept that I didn't know everything. But I also wanted to ridicule him for being different. It was tricky, for sure.

Driving to Orange County was an ordeal, especially given the sleep-deprived state I was in. Everything bothered me. The heat of the sun's rays hitting my bare arms, the droning of the tires against the pavement, the smell of stale air filtering through my air conditioner. Things that I might've forgiven if I was in a better mood were now unpardonable sins. The jerking of my car's manual transmission made it feel like a boat being tossed at sea.

"Only drive cars with a clutch," I remember my father once telling me as he struggled to find a radio station while also working the stick shift. "When you drive an automatic, you only need one arm and one leg. But with a stick, all four of your limbs are engaged, so there's more ways for the car to talk to you." That's the last thing I wanted now was a conversation with a car.

Master Huang's neighborhood was predominantly Chinese, and this was obvious not just from the people walking on the streets but also from the signage written on the strip malls. Everything was in Chinese characters. It was like I had journeyed to an exotic, distant world in order to be treated by a sacred friar. It was this theatricality that convinced me that Master Huang's treatment might actually work. The bullshit, as it so often does, gave me hope. But that went out the window when I finally arrived at the address Cynthia gave me. It was just a regular office plaza. Other than the street number, there wasn't even a marking on the door. Where was the ancient curse engraved in stone? And why didn't the entranceway look like a dragon's mouth? Instead, there was just a narrow hallway leading to a courtyard lined with azaleas someone bought at Home Depot. It was all so ordinary and disappointing.

The reception area was equally underwhelming—just a few upholstered chairs, magazines on a coffee table, and a clerk behind a counter. She was a humorless woman in her 60s and spoke with a thick Chinese accent. She seemed resentful that I required her to speak English instead of Mandarin. When I looked around, I could see why. I was the only one in the room who wasn't Asian.

I noticed an elderly man sitting almost behind the open door, which is why I missed him when I first walked in. At his side was a rooster in a cage. An honest-to-goodness rooster. Or maybe it was a hen—I'm not a zoologist. But seeing that little chicken gave me hope again. Who brings a bird to a medical appointment? Was it wrong to wonder if it was payment? Or was it simply a pet that he had a co-dependent relationship with? The woman who cuts my hair once brought her dog to work. He was a little pug that was inbred so many times his eyes popped out of his head—like he'd just seen a naked lady for the first time. She apologized for bringing her dog in, but was worried about leaving it home alone all day. Were chickens the same way? What happens if you leave a chicken in a cage in front of the TV? Do they taste different?

"Payment?" asked the woman at the counter, and I pulled out my credit card.

"Cash only," she barked.

How could Master *Huang* not accept Master*Card?* I mean, that should be a slam dunk.

"But you do accept rooster?" I wanted to say.

"Two things you must know," said the receptionist, sternly. She looked up from her paperwork and stared me down. "One, treatment will hurt."'

"Whoa, whoa ... The treatment's going to hurt?!" That definitely got my attention. I wasn't expecting that moving my qi around would hurt. I mean, it's just made up, right?

"And two," she said with great import, "no one speaks to Master Huang."

"No one speaks to Master Huang?"

"No one."

"Do some people speak to Master Huang?"

'No one!"

"How about you? Do you speak to Master Huang?"

"No one speaks to Master Huang."

I paused to consider if I should push this any further. I was definitely approaching the edge. Still, I felt like I could go just a few more inches.

"Is Master Huang in the room right now?" I looked toward the ceiling, as if he were a ghost instead of a real person. "Is that why you're being as cagey as that rooster?"

I was actually encouraged by the fact that no one was allowed to speak to him. It made Master Huang sound like he was the Wizard of Oz—someone I wasn't worthy of meeting. But, through his grace, he might still send me home with a working brain instead of a sackful of straw.

"Okay," I agreed. "I won't speak to Master Huang. But neither can you."

I was led into Master Huang's consultation room. It was sparsely decorated, which made it feel temporary, like he was barely one step ahead of the law. This, too, I found encouraging—as if his knowledge was too advanced for Western civilization to handle. The only thing hanging on the wall was a large poster, written in Chinese, showing the energy meridians of the human body. Were it not for that one, magical element, you could have easily thought you were in the coat-check room at the Hyatt Regency. Same carpeting too. It was ornately patterned, the kind they use to hide stains, and the walls were painted a peachy-rose color. The label on the paint can would call it something trite, like "Nutmeg Frost."

The receptionist instructed me to sit on a cushioned high-back chair, which also looked like it had been borrowed from the Hyatt Regency. Then she exited, leaving me alone with my restless brain. I sat for a good 10 minutes, anxiously awaiting the great Master's arrival. I wondered how he would diagnose me, given that no one had me fill out any paperwork describing my symptoms, nor was I allowed to talk to him. Would he read my mind? And if so, were there thoughts that I should tuck away so he couldn't get at them, like the PIN number to my bank account or the comment I made about the rooster in the waiting room? I wondered how Master Huang became a master. That's not a title the Western world is all that familiar with. Was there an exam he had to pass? Or maybe an ordeal?

I wanted to leave. It was bad enough to pay for this nonsense, but to actually wait around for it? Just as I was deciding to cut my losses and walk out, the chattering of my exhausted brain was interrupted by something absolutely incredible. Almost horrific. Just the thought of it still terrifies me. It was a violent, distant rumble, and I lurched in my chair when I heard it. It didn't sound like a car or a truck passing on the street. It was deeper. Like the earth was opening up from beneath the sea floor. The door to the office slowly cracked open, and in tumbled a layer of cold fog. It was wispy at first, but it grew thicker as it pushed its way toward me. I could feel my heart race as the evil smoke billowed into a cloud. Four feet tall it stood, just a few inches from my face. Sparks of lightning shot toward the walls, and from that angry and tempestuous cloud emerged an elderly, robed man with a long, dark mustache. He was floating in midair. It was Master Huang.

Okay, that's complete bullshit. It wasn't anything close to this. Here's what really happened. The door, which hadn't been oiled in years, simply squeaked open, revealing a doughy, middle-aged Asian man in a tracksuit. He held a large plastic cup of soda from McDonald's, and he lumbered in, arriving a few seconds after his gut, which he was working on supersizing. This was the great Master Huang. Not an ancient sorcerer, but some schlub who looked like he sold stereo equipment from the back of a van. I spent $300 for this?!

I tried to make eye contact with him, but instead he kept his gaze focused on the distance behind me, as if he was looking through me. Master Huang clapped his hands loudly and rubbed them together like he was trying to start a fire. No hello. No acknowledgement of my presence. He didn't even ask what brought me there. Had he, I would've responded, "I was carried in the mouth of a giant pelican, you fucking quack." I had opened my mind to try something new, and for that, I was made to feel like a fool. Well, I wasn't going to let him get away with it. Not today. Not ever, really. That's why I decided that, despite it being forbidden, I was going to speak to Master Huang.

"Master Huang," I said very casually. "I'm told this treatment can be very painful."

Master Huang stopped rubbing his palms together and stared at me. His cheeks fell, and his thin lips pursed, outraged that I had the temerity to address him. There would be hell to pay for this—I could see it in his eyes. The receptionist would be tied to the floor with long, red silks. Corn kernels would be glued to her eyelids, and, at his command, the rooster would be released from its cage, like the kraken. Famished from days of not being fed, it would peck at her eyeballs while she screamed in agony. Order would be restored. Master Huang would see to that. But to me, he said not a word. So I continued.

"No matter how painful it is, Master Huang — no matter how much I beg or plead, do not stop the treatment."

Master Huang scowled impatiently, then dug the tip of his thumb into the bottom of my foot. His finger was extraordinarily strong from years of manipulating people. It was thick, like a telephone pole, and the pressure from it made it feel like I had jumped onto a railroad spike.

"Master Huang!" I screamed. "I'm begging you: STOP THE TREATMENT!"

The corner of Master Huang's mouth slowly turned upward. His eyes flashed a twinkle of life. He tried to fight it, but his magic was no match for mine. It only lasted a second or two, but I saw it on Master Huang's face. He was laughing, and he resented me for it.

Master Huang said nothing, and stormed out of the room. I shook my head in disbelief.

"Grabbing some more energy from the supply closet?" I called off. "It's next to the coffee filters."

A few minutes later, Master Huang returned, stone-faced, determined to blow past my nonsense. He continued the treatment, which was basically just 30 minutes of him burrowing his thumb deep into my body, then declaring that my kidneys were clear.

"My kidneys? I'm here for insomnia, not an adverse reaction to grape juice!" I left in a huff, having thoroughly debunked Master Huang, and it only cost me $300 to do so.

When I returned home, I told Cynthia of the joke that broke Master Huang, and she shook her head. I guess I was expecting a different reaction from her because she's always been my biggest fan. But this time she was disappointed. I had voluntarily signed up to try something new, but I hadn't given it a fair shot. I was stuck in fear and arrogance, and it wasn't serving me. That night, a few hours after falling asleep, the voice in my head woke me up again. It just wouldn't stay quiet.

"I have someone else for you to see," said Cynthia a few days later, while I was brewing my third cup of coffee. "But you have to keep an open mind this time."

"Uh-huh. And who's this guy, a shaman from the Yucatán Peninsula?"

She paused before answering, because that's almost exactly who he was.

"He's a healer."

I grumbled, then agreed to go, and with a better attitude. I knew she was right—that I had to try something new—but I still found it to be so difficult. It's the reason why, as a child, I spent far too many years swimming in the kiddie pool of our local recreation center instead of the regular pool. It felt safer in the kiddie pool, even though I knew it was half filled with piss. Maybe I was an optimist. Maybe I preferred to think of it as half empty of piss.

It didn't hurt that the drive to the healer was much shorter. He worked out of his house, in the next town over, on a street that didn't have a name but a number. Like Avenue 42, or something like that. In Manhattan, it's normal for streets to be named after numbers, but in Los Angeles it can be a signal to roll up your windows. It's like whoever was supposed to choose creative street names decided, "Screw it, this is not where I want to die."

When I finally found a parking spot, it was in front of a run-down house with a chain-link fence separating the garbage on the sidewalk from the garbage in the front yard. Maybe they thought that without the fence, someone might steal the cinder blocks and old rubber tires in front of the house. A heavily tattooed man worked on his car, which was parked on the dirt patch where a lawn once grew. He eyed me as I locked my car, wondering if I came to buy drugs.

"What do you need? Smack, China White, Purple Drank?"

"I need to sleep, so I'm thinking Ambien. Maybe chamomile, if you have some. In other words, either a dime bag or a tea bag."

I scrambled a few blocks until I arrived at the healer's home. Robert was his name, and he lived in a small row house with flimsy walls that looked like they had been made from hardened cream cheese. I knocked once, then again a few seconds later.

"Hurry up," I thought while scanning for any murderers behind me. Unlike my opinion of Master Huang, I didn't really have a preconceived notion of what a healer was supposed to look like. Somebody in a grass skirt, maybe. Perhaps a helmet that looks like a buffalo. The guy who answered the front door wasn't wearing any of this. He was as plain as could be. Just an ordinary man in his late 30s, with messy blond hair, wearing a T-shirt, jeans and flip-flops.

"Come on in!" He said it with a warm smile and Southern accent. This threw me for a loop. Without an air of pretentiousness, I wasn't sure I'd be able to mock him.

"Sorry about the smell," he said as I followed him into his living room. "I'm making chili." There were pillows arranged in a circle on the floor, and a guitar was resting against the couch. Maybe it was drum circle, or a trust circle. Any time someone invokes that shape, I want to run. Too much caring and sharing. Robert stopped in the kitchen for a moment to lower the burner.

"The secret is just a hint of maple syrup, but I shouldn't be telling you that, though. It's my granny's recipe."

He spoke to me like an old friend, as if we had grown up together shootin' possum in the holler. Then I followed him down the hall, passing through his bedroom, which led into another room, which he used for an office. In college, I wouldn't have thought twice about walking into a man's bedroom. It was just someplace to hang out. But in the real world, it took on a whole different meaning. So much of life is about context. Someone should've mentioned that during our college commencement speech, instead of urging us to make the world a better place. Higher education let me down in that regard.

"Take a seat," said Robert, gesturing toward a massage table. The room wasn't so much decorated as it was collected. There was a Native American blanket draped over a chair, an Aborigine didgeridoo leaning in the corner, and a small dish filled with, what turned out to be, leaves of white mountain sage.

"My wife is going to be mad at me for saying this," I blurted, "but I don't really believe in any of this crap." I didn't mean to sound so aggressive, I just can't help myself sometimes. The words fly out of my mouth like they should be on a leash.

"What crap?" he asked.

"This crap." I pointed to all the props in the room. "The cult crap."

"Oh, okay." If Robert was hurt, he didn't seem to be. He seemed almost amused.

I proceeded to tell him what brought me here. How the worries of the world were waking me up in the middle of the night, even though I didn't know what they were. I was hoping the more clues I gave him, the easier it would be for him to find an answer. But he wasn't really interested in the details. If anything, he looked surprised that I was telling him this stuff—like it was none of his business.

"Sounds rough. Ready to go?"

"Go where?"

"The present." He said it like it was obvious.

"Um, aren't we in the present?" I asked.

"I am. You're not. Hop on."

He gestured to the massage table, then he lit a candle and asked, "Do you have any judgments against candles?"

That made me feel like an idiot. Of course I didn't have any judgments against candles. You put them on birthday cake. It's balloons that I think are a waste.

I lay down on my back, the table wobbling as I shifted to get comfortable. Robert explained that he was going to teach me an ancient yoga breath used for meditation.

"*Pranayama.* It means 'breath of the underworld,'" he said, draping a blanket over me. "People tend to get very cold."

Above my head the blades of a ceiling fan spun. "Shouldn't we turn the fan off?" I asked. "In case I start to levitate."

"That's what the rocks are for." He smiled, placing a large stone in each of my hands. "They weigh you down." Although they looked and felt exactly like ordinary rocks, he assured me they were not. They were special, having been pulled from the ocean, where the salt water imbued them with magic powers—powers that were made even stronger when he recharged them under the light of the full moon. I thought about saying something derisive about that, but opted not to, owing to the fact that he was holding a bag of rocks. Then he pulled out a leaf of sage and set it on fire with a Bic lighter. It smelled sweet—almost sacred. Combined with the Native American flute music playing in the background, it made it feel like I was in a gift shop in Sedona, and who doesn't like gift shops?

Following his instructions, I closed my eyes and began the breathing process. Two inhales—one low from the diaphragm; the other, high from the chest. Then one large exhale. Then again and again. He continued talking, adjusting my feet and shoulders while I chugged along. Then came the didgeridoo, which he blew in my direction. Its deep *woa-woa-woooaaaaaa* passed through me like radiation, and the ridiculousness of it embarrassed me.

"I'm not the kind of person who does this," I told myself while doing exactly this. The foolishness of it all made me want to run away, so I retreated further into myself, away from the didgeridoo and the smoke and the essential oils he was applying to my feet. I thought only of the instructions that he gave me. The breath.

After about 30 seconds of breathing, the world inside my head became dark and still. I was now floating in a quiet, black room, infinitely large on all ends. I wish I could remember more about it, but I think that was the point. My brain wasn't supposed to be on, commenting on the events of my life and fretting over things that hadn't yet happened. It was off. Not quite awake, but not quite asleep, I was in a third state. I was at peace, yet strangely observing it all.

Then, as quickly as it started, it was over. I recall suddenly gasping for air, as if I had just resurfaced from a long swim underwater. It was scary, actually. My eyes shot open, and I lurched up on my elbows, unsure of where I was. There was Robert sitting on a chair, reading the liner notes of the CD that was playing.

"Welcome back!" he said.

I didn't understand what he meant by that. Welcome back from where?

"The underworld!" Robert pulled the blanket off me and started folding it. Considering that I had just returned from the underworld, I was a little put off by how casually he treated the whole thing.

"Is that it? Am I done?"

"Well, yeah. You were gone for almost an hour."

"An hour??" The whole experience felt like it lasted only a few seconds.

"Towards the end, you stopped breathing for two, maybe three minutes. You were deep." He tucked the blanket under his chin and doubled it.

"Be careful sitting up. You're going to feel a little drunk."

I slowly moved to the edge of the table. He was right. I did feel drunk. So drunk that it took me several minutes just to put my shoes back on.

When I met Robert in the living room, I thanked him. But I wasn't able to offer more words than that. They just didn't come to me. He must've been expecting that, because he smiled and handed me the two rocks that I held earlier. One had a black band around it, stained by tar.

"They're yours now." I cradled them like precious gems, afraid of letting the magic slip through my fingers.

In my car, I sat for a few moments before putting the key in. The front seat seemed roomier now—like I'd lost 20 pounds, but from my soul. My hands gripped the leather steering wheel, and the stitching suddenly reminded me of the seams on a baseball. It's funny how that hadn't occurred to me before. Outside the window, the man was still working on his car, but he was no longer staring at me, wondering if I was there to buy drugs. He had softened while I was gone. Just a guy tinkering on his Mustang.

In the distance, I noticed a crow flying in the sky, but impossibly slow. It seemed to hang there in between beats of its wings, somehow finding extra time within each second ... not to fly, but just to be.

I wondered how long this feeling would last. This moment of calm. This relief from myself.

Jailbreak

In Hollywood, so much begins and ends with a "general" meeting. It works like this: You put an unemployed writer in a room with a studio executive and see what happens. Generally, nothing. I think it's just an excuse to keep people occupied. Make work for people who make believe. Unlike a pitch meeting, which essentially offers you a chance to crawl into bed with someone, a general meeting is more like a blind date. It's awkward and uncomfortable, and you usually never hear from that person again. I should mention that most screenwriters fall into the category of unemployed or soon-to-be unemployed. It's the nature of the business. We're contractors. So every few months, I put on a dress shirt and flirt with anyone who swipes right on my profile.

"Thanks for coming in. I hope traffic wasn't too bad."

"Not at all! You're just five miles away, so it only took an hour and a half."

For three decades, my writing partner and I have been taking general meetings, and secretly, I've grown to dread them. We do it because Hollywood-schmoozing is a necessary evil. Occasionally, a real job opportunity will spring from these meetings, and for that I'm grateful. But mostly it's a lot of talk with very little action. It's exposition. It's the part of the movie everyone hates.

My partner's name is Sivert, and most people are surprised to discover that Sivert is his first name, not last. It's Norwegian. I don't know what it means, but a few years ago while shopping in Ikea, I discovered that "Sivert" was the name of their lowest-priced shelving unit. He went to the store to confirm this, but by the time he got there, they'd already been discontinued.

In our case, every general meeting starts with the same routine: I spend a few minutes in my car, trying to give myself an attitude adjustment.

"Just put on a smile. Is that so hard?"

"I'm a writer, not an actor!"

"Well, you're two weeks away from being an unemployed writer, so act like you give a shit."

When the fight with myself ends, I meet Sivert in the lobby with an offering, to show that the good side of me has won. Usually, it's a memory trick to recall the name of the person we're meeting with.

"Her name is Elena," I tell Sivert. "Imagine driving in her car, swerving all over the road while you scream, 'Pick *a lane-a!*'"

I'm good at stuff like that. The more creative the visual, the easier it is to recall their name. It's practically foolproof, yet despite this, I almost never address our hosts by their name. I always second-guess myself. Is the woman driving the car Elena or Paula? As in, "Paula over!"

Sivert's half of the routine requires more preparation but less creativity. The night before, he'll get on the computer and perform a deep dive into our host's professional history. When it comes to making small talk, he likes to be prepared.

"You know that movie about the ghost kitten that becomes a submarine commander?" he says to me as we wait for the elevator. "This woman produced it."

"Never heard of it," I reply. "But it sounds dreadful."

"*Lieutenant Nine Lives.* You saw it a few years ago, on a plane to Portland. You said it was 'Oscar-worthy.'"

That's another thing about Sivert. He remembers the details of my life better than I do. I think it's because he's fully present, whereas I tend to drift. When I'm bored, my mind will take me someplace else. Usually someplace in the past, like my childhood. Of course, back then, my mind was always in the future.

Hollywood executives tend to decorate their office one of two ways: If they've been around the business for a while, they display the promotional material from the various projects they've worked on. It might be the name of a TV series on a coffee mug, or the face of an actor printed onto a basketball. Something like that. To anyone sitting on their couch, this functions as an informal résumé, and it's actually quite useful.

"*Amélie.* I loved that movie!" I once said, noticing a poster on the wall. "What did you do on it?"

The exec looked at me incredulously and responded, "I was five when that movie came out."

Okay, so they don't hire five-year-olds to work on movies. I learned something. You don't have to be snippy about it.

If they're relatively new to the business, the executive will often assert how creative they are by decorating their office like a day-care center: wall-to-wall toys, gumball machines, board games ... For all I know, there could be a Diaper Genie stashed underneath their desk for discreet calls of nature. What they don't realize is that this décor sends the exact wrong message. They think they're being creative, but they're not—they're being cliché.

So when they tell you they're looking to buy a project that's "truly unique," you know that's not what they mean.

Still, you can derive meaning from the props they display. A Nerf gun on the coffee table means the executive appreciates the art of slapstick. A lunch box with *Bewitched* on it suggests a respect for high-concept social satire. A Slinky perched on the edge of their desk is the equivalent to having a Ph.D. in *commedia dell'arte.* And if they possess all of the above, plus a tub of Lincoln Logs, you just might be in the presence of comedic greatness. Or a three-year-old.

Invariably, every meeting starts with our host asking how Sivert and I met. Since we're a writing team, it's a natural icebreaker. At the beginning of our career, I was happy to share our meet-cute. That's what screenwriters call it. It's the moment in a romantic comedy when the young hero gets into the elevator, hits on the woman next to him, only to later discover that she's his boss. "Whoops! Sorry I sexually harassed you!"

Initially, Sivert and I would share our meet-cute like the elderly couple at the end of *When Harry Met Sally.* I'd recount a detail, Sivert would correct me, and everyone would laugh. But now, after all these years, it pains me to retell it. Imagine being a professional storyteller—someone who gets paid to create new adventures—then being forced to tell the same story over and over, like two characters stuck in a Samuel Beckett play. No applause or curtain call. Just the promise that you're going to relive the same tale today, tomorrow, and the rest of your career. Obviously, there are worse fates in life, so I don't want to sound too much like a crybaby. But still, feel bad for me.

The truth is, my partnership with Sivert was borne from desperation. A few years after arriving in Los Angeles, I signed with one of the biggest TV agents in Hollywood. Her name was Barbara Cotner, and she was a middle-aged woman with a sharp tongue and commanding presence. Through a friend of a friend, I sent her one of my scripts, and when she finally read it, she excitedly called me.

"I love this! Why didn't you get this to me sooner!" she screamed into the phone. That script had been sitting on her desk for almost a year. I would later learn that Barbara had a reputation for being bananas. Rather than contradict her, I decided to evade the question.

"So do you think it's good enough to get me a staff job?"

"Why else would I be calling you! You think I'm just working my way down the fucking white pages?"

She seemed furious at me. Or overcome with joy. It was impossible to tell. I felt like apologizing, but I sensed that might further enrage her, so I decided to say nothing at all.

"Hello? Hello, are you still there?" she screeched.

"Yes, I'm still here."

"For fuck's sake, I thought you hung up. You're coming in tomorrow for a meeting. Ten o'clock."

"Okay."

"No!!! I can't do 10. How about 11:15?"

"Sure."

"I'm not talking to you. I'm talking to my assistant. Does 11:15 work?"

"Are you asking me?"

"Who the fuck else would I be asking?!"

"I'm sorry. I'm so confused!"

I began to move the phone back to the cradle, but I wasn't sure if she was done yelling at me, so I hesitated. I didn't want to be disrespectful, in case she thought of another reason to berate me. Something that she may have forgotten, or initially felt uneasy about. That's how important she was to me.

"Hang up, already! I need to make another call!" she shouted. In retrospect, our relationship may have been a little abusive.

The next day, I was sitting in the reception area of her Beverly Hills office, marveling at how quickly my fortunes had changed. Yesterday, I was a production assistant on a TV show, making coffee and photocopies. Now I was taking my very first general meeting. I was pretending to read a copy of *Variety,* when a young assistant approached me.

"Water?"

"Right away!" I almost replied. Years of working as an assistant had given me this Pavlovian instinct to fetch. Turns out, she was actually *offering me* water. It was a fancy brand. Fiji. So fancy that the bottle was square. I accepted it as if she were handing me an Oscar.

"Barbara will see you now," she said, pointing me toward her door.

Inside her office, there was a cowskin rug lying in the middle of the floor. It made me freeze in my spot. Was I supposed to walk on it? You can't just walk on a cowskin. That would ruin it. Or can you? I mean, cows are pretty common. It's not like it was the hide of a Pegasus. I wondered if Barbara killed the cow herself. Maybe it was a client that pissed her off. I decided to circumnavigate the cow, swooping past her desk before settling on the couch. Years of playing the Floor Is Lava as a child gave me this skill set.

Sitting nervously on her couch, my eyes took in the grandeur of Barbara's office. It landed on the sprawling view from her window. I could see the skyscrapers of Century City, and beyond that, the glimmering water of the Pacific Ocean.

"So this is Hollywood," I thought. Not the real Hollywood, of course. That was in a dumpy part of town you drove through with your doors locked. This was the fictional Hollywood— the glamorous version they portray in the movies.

Then I noticed that Barbara's chair was turned away from me. The back of it was high, obscuring her head. It was such a power move to not turn around and greet me when I entered, and it made me feel insignificant.

"Hi, I'm Michael." I said this quietly, as if I were defusing a bomb. There was no response, so I continued. "Thank you for bringing me in."

There was dead silence as I waited for Barbara to acknowledge my presence. Making someone wait for you is common in Hollywood. It's how executives assert their dominance. They don't even place phone calls themselves. Instead, they have their assistant call, and another assistant will answer. Then it's a game of chicken to see which assistant will have their boss pick up first. Sometimes they don't pick up at all. A few years ago, Sivert and I received a phone call from an exec we sold a pilot to. We were on hold for 10 minutes, waiting like schmucks, before the assistant finally got back on the line and said, "I'm sorry, you caught her at a bad time."

"You called us!"

Anyway, that's how I felt, waiting for Barbara Cotner to acknowledge me as I announced my presence one last time.

"It really is a pleasure."

Just then, Barbara bounded through the door.

"Who the fuck are you talking to?" she barked, startling both me and the cow rug beyond measure.

"I have no idea," I responded.

Barbara howled with laughter, and I joined in. I wasn't trying to be funny, but that was Barbara's thing. She never wanted you to think she was missing out on the joke, so when in doubt, she acted like you were kidding. So there we were, just two idiots, laughing as if something funny had been said.

Barbara took a seat at her large, mahogany desk and peered

down at me, her face illuminated by the golden reflection from its glossy surface.

"Let's stop fucking around," she said matter-of-factly. I swear to God, I was unaware that either of us was fucking around.

"Every year," she continued, "I sign one baby writer. Someone that I nurture to greatness."

She smiled at me, the way Willy Wonka smiled to Charlie when he gave him the keys to the chocolate factory.

"That baby writer is you, Michael."

She said it with such importance and tenderness, I half expected the sofa to blast through the roof, navigating its way over Victorian London while she sang "Pure Imagination." In one year, she said, I'd be staffed on a sitcom. And in three years, I'd be running my own show.

"Thank you! Thank you so much!"

"You're welcome," she responded, like it was a done deal instead of what it was—an empty Hollywood promise.

She rose to shake my hand and escorted me to the door. And just like that, our general meeting was over. Her assistant handed me my validated parking stub, now plastered in stickers. There were six of them, each one worth 15 minutes of time. One covered the actual meeting, two were for the time I spent waiting in the lobby, and three were for the time I spent waiting in my car before waiting in the lobby. These guys were tossing around money like it was confetti. As I walked toward the elevator, Barbara waved and added, "You have a rare comedic voice, Michael." Her compliment was particularly insightful, given that I had barely said two words.

I made my way to the parking garage, my feet never touching the ground. This was the first time in my life that someone blew smoke up my ass. The thick fumes kept me aloft as they drifted through my colon toward my head, which was now imagining my life as a successful television writer. It was like a magical fart, but in reverse, and the euphoria would soon wear off.

The problem with Barbara's praise was that it wasn't earned. I wasn't some great talent, and I knew it. At best, I was passable. So calling me a "rare comedic voice" sounded more like a generic press release than a genuine compliment. Instead of rejoicing about my future, I began to doubt it. Would I really be on staff of a TV show within a year? And who in their right mind would trust me to run one? After a few days of torturing myself with apprehension, I reached out to Barbara's assistant. I was hoping to get some reassurance from one of Barbara's previous baby writers. That's how I learned about Sivert. He was the guy two years before me. I wrote his name down as "Sivert Glarum," but when I read it back later, I wasn't sure if it was supposed to be "Sivert, Glarum."

I was nervous about calling him. After all, he was a lot more successful than me, and I was uncomfortable with the idea of wasting his time. I told him as much when we finally connected.

"Dude," he laughed, "I work in a fucking record store."

Unfortunately, *A Fucking Record Store* wasn't the latest turd on the Fox fall schedule. It was a low-rent storefront in Mar Vista that sold bootleg concert recordings out of the back room. I sighed. Even though I suspected everything Barbara had told me was bullshit, I wanted to believe her. I really did. Besides, there was no reason for her to lie, when I was fully prepared for the truth. I would later come to the conclusion that Barbara didn't lie out of malice, she did it out of habit. That's how people like her talked, with hype and hyperbole. This was just a story that Barbara told over and over while her mind was elsewhere—probably on a dairy farm in upstate New York, fantasizing about which bovine she'd murder next.

Now I doubted I'd have any chance at all of landing a staff job, so I asked Sivert if I could see the script that got him signed with Barbara, just for comparison. When I read it a few days later, a lump came to my throat. His script was better than the one I wrote. It was well structured, the act breaks popped, and the dialogue was sharp and natural. If that couldn't get him work, then what hope did I have? So I made him an offer—an offer to team up. He was better at story structure, but having just signed with Barbara, I was hotter than he was. There was no sense in competing against each other, especially when it's easier to get hired as a team, so we formed a partnership. In screenwriting terms, this is called the "lock." It's how unlikely friendships are formed, like Robert De Niro and Charles Grodin in *Midnight Run.* Only in our case, we weren't handcuffed, we were clinging to each other in fear.

Barbara blessed our union, and Sivert and I spent the next year writing sample scripts together. It was fun riffing off each other, building a world from scratch. That's the part that writers like—the creating. Every day after work, on weekends, and on holidays, we met. We approached our craft with a sense of urgency, knowing that Barbara would soon have a new baby writer lined up behind us.

"Type faster, monkey!" I'd snap when Sivert was at the keyboard.

We rarely heard from Barbara during that time. She never set up any job interviews, or even any general meetings. One day, her assistant reached out to us to schedule an important phone call with Barbara. On the day, Sivert and I huddled over the speakerphone, eager to soak up her attention. Did she finally get us a big break? Or maybe she had a new strategy to get us hired. In the end, the conversation was far more sobering. Since we had failed to get work, Barbara was dropping us as clients.

"But isn't that *her* job, to get us work?" I asked Sivert.

Sivert threw his pen against the wall. "I think the only reason she teamed us up was so that she could dump us with one phone call instead of two."

We now had to find a new agent, essentially starting our careers from zero again.

And that's our origin story. We've told abbreviated versions of it a billion times. Sometimes I tell that final joke, other times Sivert takes it. We know where the laughs are, and we know when to milk the emotional parts. It's a good story, but I hate telling it. I want to forget that time of my life when we struggled so hard. I don't need to relive it in a general meeting, when I'm unemployed and at my most vulnerable. I don't want to even mention it.

Despite the fact that we've been partners for half our lives, I don't share this with Sivert. You'd think I would, given that we share everything else. That comes from working on the same scripts and pouring the details of our personal lives into them. Even though he's like a brother to me now, our relationship is also professional. There's nothing to be gained by telling him how meetings like this make me feel like a prisoner in my own story, so I hide that from him. I don't think he notices, though. He's more social than I am, and he's perfectly happy making small talk with these executives.

There was a time when my mind would go someplace fictional during these meetings, like the farm in upstate New York where Barbara stalked dairy cows with a carrot peeler. But as I've gotten older, my mind retreats to my childhood home, before I moved to Los Angeles to chase a dream. That's where I was on a scorching California afternoon, captive to yet another pointless general meeting. This executive had what I initially thought were two laptops sitting on his desk, and I was impressed ... like he needed to be in constant communication with the world. Then I realized they weren't laptops—it was just a game of Battleship.

"So how did you two meet?" said our host, as if he was the first person to ask.

"H-6," I said to myself. "You sunk my will to respond."

"We were teamed up by our first agent," responded Sivert. "Barbara Cotner, if you know who she is."

I completely checked out. I began racing down an old Colonial road, past Crane's Pond, on my way home from high school. My eyes watered as the autumn air rushed into my face. It's been years since I felt that kind of wind. Not bitter cold, but crisp. As a kid, I spent hours every day just riding around the neighborhood as the harsh wind beat my knuckles for not sitting over a book while holding a pen.

"But that's just the story we tell people," Sivert interrupted. "The truth of how we teamed up is far more embarrassing."

His decision to go off-book snapped me to attention. What was he up to?

"I was at the Starbucks on Melrose buying whole beans. You know the one. Everyone there thinks they're a screenwriter, tapping away on their laptop while occasionally looking up to make sure people take notice. That's what this douchebag was doing." He gestured to me, rolling his eyes in disdain.

What the hell was he talking about? That's not how we met.

"All I want to do is pay for my coffee, but I just had to stare at this guy. I mean, the cheap bastard was taking up a table at Starbucks and he didn't even buy anything."

Why was Sivert fucking around? I didn't stop him, though. I wanted to hear more.

"And the worst part is, he had a vanilla-scented votive candle burning at his table, that he obviously brought from home."

Our host, embarrassed for me, let out a huge laugh. I laughed, too, and nodded guiltily, as if this was painfully true instead of complete fiction.

"So I have to meet this guy," he continued. "You know, just to mess with him a little bit. I go to introduce myself, but before he would talk to me, he hits save on his computer and slams it shut so that I don't steal his precious idea. Which he probably stole from *Saved by the Bell.*"

"Oh, no!" laughed our host, and a smile came to my face.

It's funny. I had always felt alone in these meetings, when my mind went elsewhere. But I was wrong. Sivert must've felt like a prisoner, too, because now he was making a run for it. He was re-writing our story, and my eyes went wide with admiration and hope.

Sivert added, "And then he kissed his finger and touched it against his laptop. Like it was the Holy Bible."

That was a nice touch, bringing religion into it. If he pitched that while I was at the keyboard, I would've typed that in for sure.

"Go, Sivert! Keep going!" I silently shouted.

This detail may have been a bit too much for the young executive, because he looked to me for confirmation. "Is this true?"

Sivert was now on the other side of the prison walls, in a clearing before the deep woods. The crazy Viking had made it, and now he wanted me to come with him. I could see it in his face.

"No, it's not true," I interjected, and Sivert winced at my betrayal. I stared at him, and I'm certain a sparkle came to my eye.

"He's only telling you half the story."

"Really?" asked the executive, growing even more engrossed.

"What my partner fails to mention is that he too was working on a screenplay in that Starbucks. *Star Tre*k fan fiction, actually."

"Fan fiction?" laughed our host.

"To be more accurate," I continued, "homoerotic fan fiction." Sivert fought to stifle a laugh.

"Not quite homoerotic," he protested. "But there was a moment between Kirk and Bones where some playful rough-housing turned into something more."

"You used the word 'bulge' a lot."

"The scene called for it!" he snapped.

By now we could barely contain our excitement. We were both outside the prison walls, running toward freedom. Creative freedom. Only a bullet fired from the highest guard tower could stop us now. And the lookout took his best shot.

"You guys are shitting me, aren't you?" fired the exec.

We both fell silent, unsure if his bullet would strike.

"Absolutely not," said Sivert.

"That's how it happened," I confirmed.

"So perfect," laughed the executive. "Absolutely perfect."

We agreed and kept running into the forest beyond.

Usually, at the end of every general meeting, Sivert and I step into the elevator and talk candidly about how it went. We discuss the plan for following up and how we'll spin this meeting to get our agent excited about us. But this time we said nothing to each other. Instead, I watched as Sivert's index finger searched for the right button. He seemed disoriented, so I reached across his body and pressed for him. Then down we went. In the underground parking lot, the only sound between us came from our footsteps as they bounced off the walls, echoing into the distance. We got into our cars, nodded goodbye, and went our separate ways.

I often think back on that day because of what it gave me, which wasn't a job but a much-needed respite from the bullshit. Despite the joy it temporarily brought us, in the years since, we've always reverted back to the original story. The true one. The one we're both so tired of telling. Sivert tells it during these general meetings, because I simply can't. I sit on the opposite end of the couch, cornered against the arm, hugging it tightly. As he drones on, I watch from the side of my eye, waiting hopefully for my brother to give me the signal to make a run for it.

"It's coming," I tell myself. "This time it's coming."

A Paper Orchestra

The greatest magic trick I ever saw was at a wedding reception. Right before dinner was served, a magician came to each table and performed a few card tricks, taking time to make small talk with everyone.

"I'd like you to pick a card, but first, your name ... "

"Amy."

"Amy. I had an aunt named Amy. She took 'aim' at 'me' with a beautiful blouse with flowers, just like yours."

As someone who writes dialogue for a living, I wanted to correct him. "Those aren't words someone might actually say." But I ignored the temptation to set him straight, the same way I ignored the floral pattern on Amy's blouse, which looked like a wreath she stole from a Thoroughbred.

"Amy, please show your card to the person sitting next to you," he continued. "What's your name, sir?"

He was pointing to me. "I am ... Douched Out. James Du Schdout." I didn't actually say that, but I smiled at the idea of saying it. There are so many things I want to say, but just don't, maybe out of fear. I think we're all like that.

"Michael," I finally blurted, and I braced for what came next.

"Michael-Michael on a unicycle, with curly hair and skin so fair." One by one, he went to every table, doing card tricks and finding tortured rhymes for everyone's name. At the end of the evening, he borrowed the D.J.'s microphone and asked everyone to stand up.

"There are approximately 125 guests at tonight's event, and I believe I've met all of you."

"Okay," I thought. "Everyone in the room hates you. What are you getting at?"

"When I point to you and call your name, please sit down."

Seriously? Did he memorize everyone's name?!

"Gary, please sit down." The magician pointed to some guy who looked surprised, then took his seat. Then he pointed to the woman sitting next to him. "Ginerva, please sit down." Ginerva smiled broadly, astonished that for the first time in her life, someone had gotten her name right. "Esteban, sit down. Shea, sit down. Lucy, sit down ... " At first, the audience reacted with quiet amazement, but that quickly turned to laughter as his feat became more and more impossible. Soon, the laughter gave way to silent self-loathing, as everyone jealously wondered how he could remember 125 names but we couldn't remember what we ordered for dinner. Was it the chicken or the fish? This went on and on, but the magician kept skipping over a tall woman in her mid-40s, whose name he was obviously struggling to recall. When she was the last person standing, he cautiously approached and studied her like a painting on a museum wall.

"Did you change your appearance since when we first met, ma'am?"

"Yes," I muttered under my breath. "She got plastic surgery while they were setting out the dinner rolls."

"What's that?"

"Nothing, Amy. Go back to your blouse."

"I was probably wearing my glasses," responded the last woman standing.

"Would you mind putting them back on?" The audience waited with bated breath as she placed her glasses over her eyes, changing everything. A big smile of relief came to the magician's face.

"Carolyn, sit down!" And the crowd burst into cheers.

It's no giant secret how he did it. It was just a matter of burning a name into his head and linking it to some small trigger in their appearance, then doing it 124 more times. But it was extraordinary to watch. Absolutely amazing. He's probably the greatest magician I've ever seen. If only I could remember his name.

That right there is my problem. There are so many moments of my life that I simply don't remember, or remember wrong. An old friend might recount a hilarious story, and I'll laugh, as if it was the craziest thing I've ever heard. Then he'll remind me that not only was I there, I was the one who did it! And then my laughter turns to embarrassment. Why can't I be trusted with my own memories?

When I was a junior in college, I spent a semester in Spain. The stories I could tell would make you howl with delight ... if only I could remember them. Sure, I recall bits and pieces, but not enough to make a narrative out of it. I do remember renting a room from a widow who was raising her two teenage daughters. Her name was Maria Angeles, and even though she had dozens of students moving in and out of her small apartment, I could tell she liked me more than most. We'd hang out in the kitchen, like a couple of chatty Spanish housewives, while she taught me how to prepare a proper *tortilla de patatas.* It all comes down to *la vuelta,* as she called it. The flip. It's the moment of reveal that everything leads up to. After having spent so much time cooking the potato-and-egg mixture, would the underside be what you hoped it would be? Would it be crispy and golden, or just burned and ruined? *La vuelta.*

We went to the market together, Maria Angeles and I, and she invited me to tea at her sister's home ... I was one of the girls. And when we learned that her 14-year-old daughter, Carmen, was going on a date, we both insisted on meeting the boy first.

"I'm your mother!" shouted Maria Angeles.

"And I'm your American!"

I don't know what happened next, but that's typical of my memories of Spain. Fragments, just not the whole picture. If only I had kept a diary, I could point to a specific story and extrapolate the profound impact it had on my life—like a TED Talk.

I remember sharing that story with my college girlfriend back in New Jersey. Her name was Jessica, and with her porcelain skin and jet-black hair, she looked like a French model. Not the snobby, eating-disorder kind. She was the friendly, cute kind that exists only in movies.

The first time I saw Jessica was at a Thanksgiving dinner hosted by my mother's friend. I could barely make eye contact, she was so pretty. That probably made me appear introspective and complex, instead of what I really was—awkward and wilting. We spoke for a few minutes, then she disappeared with her handsome boyfriend, who himself looked like he jumped off a movie screen. So I was shocked when, in February, a handwritten letter from her arrived at my dorm room. She said she was moving nearby and we should get together sometime. I checked the envelope to make sure it was addressed to me. Her handwriting wasn't in cursive. Instead, she used old-fashioned block print, so that each letter got its own space. It must've taken more time that way, and I was flattered.

On the day we hung out together, she mentioned that she had since broken up with her boyfriend. Sensing an opening, I worked up the courage to say, "What's his number? I'm gonna ask him out."

Jessica laughed and immediately fell in love with me. I took things a little slower, waiting until the rest of the afternoon to fall in love with her. Our relationship became serious. It wasn't the kind of love that older people have, where they're obliged to schlep to the drugstore to pick up cold medicine for their spouse. This was much better love. Passionate and exciting better love. Our relationship was like a furnace, consuming our outside interests so it could burn white-hot. When you're young like that, everything gets sacrificed to the flame.

In public, I felt great about myself, enjoying how impressed people were that someone like me could get someone like her.

"Is she a hostage?" a waitress might ask. "Blink if you're in danger, honey."

There was a balmy, summer night we spent on the Jersey Shore. We shared an ice-cream cone while we sat on the beach watching the waves crash. The cool ocean breeze brushed against our faces, and we dug our feet into the warm sand, as if that would anchor us there forever. It was a wonderful moment that I ruined by telling Jessica that I'd be spending part of junior year abroad. We were both heartbroken. I'd been looking forward to it for years, but now that I found someone who completely understood me, leaving her felt like a terrible idea. Without her, how could I breathe? It was only for a few months, but at that age, love feels like life support.

While in Spain, we both counted the days until my return. We sent letters to each other every day, and we swore our undying love. Exactly one year later, she was swearing her undying love to someone else, and I collapsed, having been kicked in the heart. The breakup took me by complete surprise. It wasn't like we constantly fought or bickered. There was none of that. She just found someone else and decided it was time to move on. There was barely even a goodbye. When the nuclear reactor blew up in Chernobyl, residents grabbed a few personal items and got the hell out as fast as they could. They didn't even finish the food on their plate. That's how Jessica dropped me—faster than a bowl of radioactive soup.

As soon as the shock of the breakup wore off, I fell into a deep depression. It was a pit of sadness so profound, I felt like I was at the bottom of a well, where everything around me was cold and dark. My heart gave up, and I followed.

"How could she possibly continue her life without me! Well, *I* won't!"

And so I sat, wounded and alone in the hole I had dug for myself, replaying the key moments of our relationship. Sometimes I'd look for clues as to why she broke up with me; other times I did it just to see her face again. The memories would fall on my head, bathing me like raindrops on a hot summer day. At first they were cool and comforting, but after a few minutes, I was drenched with sorrow. I wondered how she could've done this to me, and began to doubt whether my memories of Jessica were even true. Did my brain create a fictionalized version of her?

Back then, I was taking a class in abnormal psychology. "Nuts and Sluts" is what everyone called it. The danger of taking such a class is that it's easy to diagnose yourself with whatever disorder you're studying. One week I had borderline personality, and the next I was a sociopath. But things really came into focus when I accidentally did the supplemental reading on how memories work. According to the article that I didn't need to read, each time you recall a memory, you're not recalling the original event but rather the last time you recalled it. So the memory itself morphs, like a game of telephone, until it eventually becomes whatever your brain wants it to be. It's why eyewitness accounts can be so untrustworthy. It occurred to me that the trick my memory was creating was far more impressive than the one the magician performed. He only recalled 125 names. I created an entire relationship.

I had an empty shoebox, where I stored old photos of me and Jessica, cards she gave me, keepsakes of our relationship ... stuff like that. Every time I saw that shoebox, it would wreck me. Eventually, I gathered enough emotional strength to just toss it in the garbage. That was a hard thing to do.

When I moved to Los Angeles, after college, it was to pursue a career in TV writing. But it was also to put distance between me and Jessica. I was running to something, but in truth, I was also running away from something. Hollywood, in my mind, seemed like the perfect place for the "new me" to emerge. Swimming pools, movie stars, and all the other trappings that the Beverly Hillbillies enjoyed. Sadly, the first thing I noticed when I drove across the state line was just how dry everything was. The land felt foreign to me, and I wondered how long New Me could last here.

Despite my trepidation, I actually did pretty well. I got a job writing on a show called *Just Shoot Me,* and it was there that I met a pretty guest star named Cynthia. We hit it off instantly, even though I was still finishing my groundbreaking research in the field of self-pity. Like me, Cynthia had a vulnerability about her. But somehow hers looked like strength, whereas mine felt like weakness. This became most obvious whenever uncomfortable emotions arose. Whereas someone else might change the subject and run away in fear, Cynthia always held her ground—acknowledging it, dealing with it, then letting it pass. When it came to difficult feelings, she was a matador in the ring.

On our third date, she invited me to dinner at her apartment, in Hollywood. I discovered that even though she was in her early 30s, in some ways she lived like a child. I watched uneasily as she sautéed vegetables in a pan with a wobbly handle. It rocked from side to side, threatening to spill cooking oil onto the flames. I have no right to criticize anyone in the kitchen. I need a recipe to make tap water, but I do know a fire hazard when I see one. It's something both of my parents would've scolded me for.

"Why isn't anyone looking after her?" I wondered. A few weeks into our relationship, I made it my business to be that person. At Target, I bought her a gift. Something to keep her safe. I was almost too embarrassed to give it to her the next time we met. I tucked it inside a brown shopping bag, like something your grandfather might bring on a Sunday visit. Maybe a loaf of rye bread, or a dozen eggs he couldn't fit in his fridge.

"Ooh, what is it?" Cynthia asked, excitedly. Immediately, I felt stupid, thinking it should have been a Vermont Teddy Bear or a dozen roses.

"It's nothing really ... It's just something I noticed you didn't have." I cringed at how unromantic my gift was. It was more a representation of my anxiety than anything else.

She opened the bag and pulled out my fabulous gift. It was a fire extinguisher.

"Maybe just keep it in your kitchen." I said. "Not that you'll ever need it."

The smile fell from her face. It wasn't what she was expecting, and I sensed what I thought was disappointment. She walked toward me, then hugged me tight. I could feel her tears against my cheek as she squeezed me, and I was confused. It was just a fire extinguisher. I'd later learn that it was the first time in her life that she felt cared for. Imagine waiting a whole lifetime to feel that.

A house and two kids later, I was working on a project and I realized the stories from my time in Spain might help. I didn't keep a diary back then, but I did send daily letters to Jessica. I sent them on thin, onionskin paper that was so delicate, you almost had to be careful what you wrote. It would've been 30 years since she received those letters, but if I asked, maybe she'd recall something about that time that might spur my own memories.

According to Facebook, which is the source of all information impartial and true, Jessica was now happily married, with two kids. Surprisingly, even though we lived in New Jersey when we dated, we were now both living in Los Angeles, only a few miles apart. All my running away from her, and there she was, right behind me. I considered calling her, but stopped myself.

"Jessica, it's Michael Jamin," I thought of saying.

But what if she responded with, "I'm sorry. Michael Jamin from ... ?"

I didn't think she had completely forgotten who I was. That would be really crazy. But what if it didn't generate the reaction I wanted? It had to be more than just warm. It had to be effusive. Anything less would just confirm what I had grown to suspect—that my memories of her weren't really true, and that I was never special, just one in a series of relationships she had. And if that was the case, I didn't need to know.

This was too much for me to process on my own, so I floated the idea past Cynthia during one of our walks.

"I'm thinking of reaching out to Jessica. To see what she can tell me about the time when I lived in Spain."

"I love it. You have to!" She said it without a moment's hesitation, which threw me for a loop. She didn't give it enough agonizing or hand-wringing.

"Why?" I asked.

"Are you kidding? This is a window to your past. You'll learn something about yourself. How often do you get that chance?" That's the problem with Cynthia. If it's about exploring an emotion, or opening yourself up to vulnerability, she'll push you out of an airplane. I started to back away from the idea, but Cynthia just repeated, "You have to," as if my life depended on it. Here I was, toying with the idea of connecting with an old girlfriend, yet my wife was the one saying, "Trust me."

* * *

It's a scorching autumn morning. The sun has barely cleared the treetops, but already it's sucking moisture out of the air like a clothes dryer. It makes the skin on my knuckles hurt as they bend around the steering wheel. I'm pulling up to Jessica's house. She suggested I come at nine A.M., and even though it's only a 10-minute drive, I don't want to be late. So here I am—15 minutes early. I think that's a new addition to my personality since Jessica knew me. Anxiety. I don't remember being this anxious when I was young, but maybe I was. Whatever—I can worry about that later. I'll make time.

Of course I can't knock on her door this early. There was once a time when I could've just walked right in and plopped myself on her couch. But not anymore. That's not even an option. It's weird how two people can be so close, then life happens, and they become complete strangers. I'll just sit in my car until I'm fashionably late. Like two minutes late. Fashionably late?! I don't talk like that! I'll be one minute late. I can't park here, though. That would be weird. I'll park a few houses down, in front of that lady taking out her garbage. She looks creeped out by me, but I don't have the bandwidth to worry about her feelings too. Deal with it, Lydia.

"Why am I *really* here?" I ask myself. This isn't about getting details from an overseas trip. If it were that, I wouldn't be nervous. Cynthia is right—I'm here for something else, and I now realize what it is. I want an answer to a question that I've been carrying around for so many years. Just give me the answer, Jessica, and then I'll leave.

The clock in my car turns to 9:01. Enough. I hop out and walk toward her place. How's my hair?

Damn, the houses here are nice. Expensive. You're doing well if you live here. Hers is an old Craftsman, twice the size of our house. Maybe more. Fuck this—her husband is running laps around me. I should turn around. What?! Don't even think about turning around. You still have so much hair. That counts for something, champ. Make sure she sees the hair.

I press the doorbell. It's an impressive chime. It sounds like someone noteworthy has arrived at the door. What a bait and switch this is gonna be.

The woman down the street is staring at me. "Hi, Lydia. You can stop looking now."

Jessica swings open the door, and I realize I haven't given any thought as to what I should do next. What's the right way to greet someone you were in love with 30 years ago? It's not a handshake. God, no, that would be awful. A hug would be fine. Hugs can be intimate or they can be collegial ... there's a whole range of hugs that are appropriate for every occasion. Even football players hug. But now that moment has passed, and I'm just standing here. I should've just hugged her right when she opened the door.

"Should we high-five?" I offer.

She smiles and brings me in for a hug. Okay, good idea. Sometimes a hug is just a hug.

She's now giving me a tour of her home. It's exactly the setting I'd write in a script if I wanted the main character to feel insecure about his station in life. Hardwood floors and custom built-ins from the turn of the century. I don't really want a tour, but I say I do out of politeness.

"Relax," I tell myself. "There's time to get what you want."

It's a lovely home. Lots of original charm. Boy, she did well. I compliment her on it, so she doesn't pick up on my insecurity. I find myself stepping lightly on the floor, like walking through a museum. I've never made a trip like this before—a trip so far into the past—but I'm careful to remain in the present. I'm trying to observe all of my feelings, the way Cynthia instructed.

"Your house is amazing. I love it!"

"We got lucky. We bought it in foreclosure, so it was great deal."

"That's smart!"

I'm only pretending to know that it's smart. I know nothing about real estate. Maybe it's stupid to buy a house in foreclosure. Like it's less expensive because it comes with a ghost. That's something you'd regret in the middle of the night, when a phantom throws a candlestick at your head. I just *had* to buy a house in foreclosure!

"The piano and guitar are my husband's. He's very musical." I nod again. Seriously? You're going to talk about your husband? Why do you think I want to know more about him, or even anything about him? Even though he's not the guy Jessica dumped me for, in my mind he is, and the mention of him takes me back half a lifetime. Did you cry after we broke up? I cried. I cried every last tear in my body, until I was as dry and withered as a houseplant on a windowsill. And just when I started to perk up, I'd sit alone in my car and play the saddest songs I could find on a constant loop. U2's "One" ... Bonnie Raitt's "I Can't Make You

Love Me" ... that became the soundtrack to my misery because that's what music does. It keeps us there when we're not ready to go.

"I like your sweater," she says. I'm glad she noticed, and now I'm hoping she'll compliment me on something else. Anything, really. Like the number of fingers on my hand.

It's such an oddly insecure thought to have, especially given how happy my life turned out. I constantly tell Cynthia how grateful I am for her. We don't travel much separately, but whenever she gets on a plane without me, I worry about it crashing. I know it's unlikely, but I also know what it's like to lose someone I love. I can't live at the bottom of a well again. I wasn't strong enough the first time. So I leave something personal in her luggage. Usually, it's an old silver dollar, or a small rock that I polished. It comes with a note that's almost threatening in tone.

"This isn't yours. Bring it back to me."

So I'm not the unconfident, loveless one who needs reassuring as I walk through Jessica's dining room, with the fancy leaded-glass windows. It's the version of me that Jessica tossed away years ago—-he's the one who needs it.

"This is the sunroom," she says. "When it's nice, we spend all of our time here."

"I can see why."

Jessica isn't how I remembered her. Given that it's been 30 years, how could she be? Her hair is graying, and she wears it differently, but it's her energy that has changed the most. She's a mother now and she gives off that vibe. Concerned. Responsible. Her head seems to be elsewhere at times. Mothers always have a million things to worry about. What's she thinking about now? Do I dare ask her? She dresses differently. More conservative. Back in the day, she was edgier. Two steps ahead of what everyone else was wearing. Maybe that got tiring and people finally caught up to her. She wears glasses now with thick, oversize frames. I see lots of women wearing glasses like this. I don't like them. It draws attention away from their faces, hiding their most important feature—their eyes. When my daughter was a toddler, I once read her a picture book about a tiger. There was pivotal moment in the story, but the illustrator drew the tiger with its face turned away, so you couldn't see his eyes. Without that, there was no way of knowing how the tiger felt. Was he mad, or was he resigned? This really upset my daughter because she wanted to understand him.

"I can't see the eyes!" Lola cried. She turned the page, hoping to see the tiger's face on the opposite side of the paper, but the story had moved on. "I can't see the eyes!"

I want Jessica to remove her glasses so I can see her eyes. Is it rude to ask her to take off her glasses? If I did ask, she'd probably laugh. "I won't be able to see you then." And how would she see me? I'm also a very different person today than I was in college. But how different? As we travel through life, there are parts of ourselves that we hang on to, and parts that we let go of. We have to, to make room for new stuff. I'm still me, but I'm also not me. I hope she takes off her glasses. I'd like to see her eyes.

We're in the backyard now, underneath the canopy of two ancient trees soaring high above the roof of her house. They're too massive to even take in.

"Look at these incredible camphors," I say.

"Wow, you really know your trees!"

I don't. I just know the names of certain trees. That part of me is definitely new to Jessica. The guy who notices trees. A few years ago, I downloaded an app that identifies them. The incessant sunshine of Southern California wears me down. I become less myself. Certain trees, like camphors, offer so much shade. It's the shade that saves me. Learning the names of these trees is how I thank them.

Jessica walks back to the house, but I stop to imagine the sound the raindrops must make when they hit the leaves. It almost never rains in Southern California, and when it does, I run to the window to watch. Sometimes, I'll get inside my car and drive around, searching for a good tree to stand underneath. The leaves here are different than they are on the East Coast, where I grew up. They're smaller and waxier, so the sound of raindrops hitting them isn't quite the same, but still, they make music.

The loud ones fall from the clouds high in the air, pounding like a timpani. But others slip gently from leaves that are just a few inches above—a shushing rake on a snare drum. Close your eyes and the leaves play for you. A paper orchestra, so delicate yet full.

"If I lived here," I call out, "I'd make you stand outside with me on rainy days until we were soaked."

I'm wondering if she'll ask me why, but Jessica doesn't take the bait. She doesn't want to know me that well anymore, so she keeps her distance. When we were together, she would've been curious. She would've wanted to know everything about me. But maybe I'm wrong. Maybe my memories have been lying to me.

"We bought the hot tub a few years ago," she says, pointing to a small, above-ground pool at the edge of her yard. "We thought the kids would like it, but we almost never use it. Too much work."

"Really?"

"Yeah, you have to treat the water, then you have to heat it for a few hours, then by the time it's ready ... "

Jessica's doing a lot of this now—talking about nothing, really. Is it my fault? Am I not talking enough? I tend to get quiet. Sometimes when I'm uncomfortable, I completely shut down. I become a painting in a haunted house with eyes that follow you. But I don't think that's the case now. I want to talk to Jessica. I want to open up. Maybe it's my presence that's making her nervous. It has to be weird to have me here in her home. Or maybe Jessica is confiding in me. Could that be it? Is this stuff she's never told anyone else but, because we once loved each other, she trusts me with? What an honor. My old girlfriend has chosen me, of all people, to share her most intimate thoughts about ... hot tubs.

"Not to mention the cover. Taking it off is a hassle, and after you get out of the tub, you're cold and wet, and the last thing you want to do is put the cover back on ... "

She's still going on about the hot tub, and it makes me feel alone. Even worse, abandoned. But is that how I feel now, or is that just a remnant of how I felt 30 years ago? Either way, I'm standing right here, but Jessica is somewhere else. I don't blame her, though. Maybe I shouldn't be here, either.

We're back inside now, and we pass her teenage daughter in the hallway. I try not to stare, but she looks so much like Jessica when I knew her.

"This is Mae," she says, and her daughter gives a slight smile. She's more interested in whatever's on her phone. Still, I feel guilty, like I'm keeping a giant secret from her.

"I bet you're wondering who I really am," I say to her with my eyes. She doesn't care. She probably thinks I'm a tax consultant or a financial planner meeting with her parents. Something grown-up and impossibly boring. My sweater seems to be in on the joke, but at least her mother likes it. I'm relieved when Mae continues on her way.

I whisper to Jessica, "How much money did you save by giving her your face?" She laughs. I wonder if one day, years from now, something might trigger a memory in Mae.

"Do you remember that man I met on the staircase that day?" she'd say to her mother. "The one who stared at me. What was that all about?"

How would Jessica respond? Would she say I was just someone she once knew? Is that the story she'd tell?

This is the staircase to the basement, where all the scary things hide, and it's the last stop on the tour. I'm leaving soon, so I try to soak it all in, hoping to find what I'm looking for. Her basement is surprisingly comfy, with family photos displayed on the shelves. One in particular catches my attention. It's a picture of Jessica standing next to her husband. They're both smiling. He's smiling. She's smiling. But something about it bothers me, and I move a little closer.

"Why am I drawn to this?" I ask myself. Then I realize. His arm is draped around her shoulder. It doesn't look right. Almost cordial.

"You're doing it wrong," I say to myself. "Put your arm around her waist and pull her in tight."

I'm surprised that this bothers me, but it does. He should hug her the way I used to hug her. I know it's wrong for me to think this. You can't learn anything about someone's relationship from one photo, and how is it any of my business? And yet I like thinking this way. It feels good to be protective of something that's no longer mine.

"We can stop looking now!" yells Jessica.

I'm busted—caught red-handed, making unsubstantiated judgments about her personal life.

I turn toward her, my mind scrambling for an excuse. I'm relieved to discover she's not referring to me but a small, vintage suitcase she found in a closet. She carries it to the couch.

"Come have a seat," she says. I pause for a moment. Do I sit on the couch next to her, or take one of the chairs? The choice sends a message. The man I am sits on the chair, appropriate and at a distance. The man I used to be sits next to her, on the couch. Who am I at this moment?

I don't want to take too long, so I sit on the couch. Not too close, though. Just out of reach. I think back to that hot summer night we spent on the Jersey Shore boardwalk, the cool mist from the ocean kissing our necks. We stopped to play the carnival games. It didn't matter that they were rigged so that we never stood a chance at winning. Isn't young love the same way—doomed the minute it starts? I hugged her tight, with the smell of popcorn and caramel apples in the air. It wasn't enough to be close back then. We wanted to be so close that we were practically on the other side of each other. But now I wonder if that was really the case or if it's just an invention of my memory. I realize there are three versions of that night on the boardwalk: my version, her version, and the version that actually happened. Mine is perfect, though. If Jessica could get inside my head and watch it like an old movie, she'd absolutely love it. I'm not sure I'd want to see hers.

Jessica removes her glasses for the first time and sets them on the couch. She slowly opens the suitcase.

"I kept everything," she says with reverence, revealing a bundle of letters that I sent her from Spain. A ribbon holds them together to keep them from scattering, the way memories so easily do. I'm surprised to see how well she cared for them, and for so many years, tucked safely away in the darkest, farthest corner of her home. She reaches into the suitcase, then stops herself, almost afraid to touch them. It's the moment of the big reveal. *La vuelta.*

"Thank you for these," she says, quietly.

There's a tenderness in her voice, and even though it's been 30 years since last I heard it, I instantly recognize it. I've finally gotten what I came for. It rings like the sound of a single drop of rain, isolated from the millions.

We look at each other, a stack of yellowing papers between us —each note so delicate yet full. It feels different with Jessica now, and her eyes begin to water. In her hands she holds the remnants of someone she once loved. It's sacred and mournful. I try to think of something kind to say. Something intimate and true. But instead I say nothing and just hold this moment in my head—content to be remembered.

Alone

There's a television show where they abandon survivalists in separate locations deep in the wilderness. Each contestant gets 10 different pieces of survival gear, in addition to several cameras to record their adventures, as well as probable death due to mishap or starvation. Watching it makes me feel like a Roman emperor presiding over a gladiator fight. I pretend to be interested in the sport, but honestly, I'm just waiting for some guy to reach into a shrub for a berry, then scream in horror as a wolf chews his arm off. That's why I protest when a trained survivalist prematurely taps out due to physical anguish.

"What about *my* needs?" I shout. "There's nothing else on!"

The program I'm referring to is called *Alone,* and ironically, it's one of the few shows that I try to watch with someone else. Specifically, my daughter Lola. It's our show.

Years ago, it was easy to get her to sit with me. I'd call, and Lola would come running in. That, in and of itself, is something to see. Lola has a smile that can light up a room. I know that sounds cliché, and I'm aware that I'm biased, but it's completely true. When she's happy, or excited, her face simply can't contain the joy. It radiates from her eyes, and when it hits the people around her, they smile, too, sensing they are in the presence of someone who can see wonder. That's how I feel when I'm around her. And if I try hard to get on her wavelength, I can sometimes see wonder, too.

With *Alone* playing on TV, Lola would lie next to me with her head on my chest, and I'd steal kisses from her cheeks as she rubbed them off with her hand. I'd pretend to be indignant.

"What, you don't think I can make more?" And I'd kiss her cheeks again as she giggled. But now that she's a high-school senior, the days of her resting in my arms seem to be over. There's just so many other things for her to do.

"I can't, Papa. I have homework."

I'm proud of her work ethic. She's responsible and trustworthy. And yet ...

"Homework is for losers," I yell back.

Sometimes it's her friends that she's too busy with. It's important and healthy for a girl her age to have these connections. And yet ...

"They don't even like you! I have to pay them to be your friends!"

"Oh my God," laughs Lola, from her heart. "You can't say that!" And our living room, which is always dark, becomes light.

On the rare occasions when Lola finds the time to join me, I feel the pressure to make watching the show as entertaining as possible. So, for example, if a contestant breaks down in tears because a fish made off with his last hook, condemning him to certain starvation, I'll equate that to the dire situation I'm in.

"This horrible throw pillow," I say while trying to get it comfortable behind my head. "It's just too damn fluffy!" Lola laughs, and suddenly, I start pitching jokes, just to get more of that smile.

"Damn, look how much weight that guy has lost," I say, pointing to one of the contestants. "Other than the vacant gaze in his eyes, he looks terrific!"

"He's starving, Papa!"

"Me too. Pass me that box of cookies."

In its many seasons, a woman has never won *Alone,* but if you ask me, the women are far more impressive than their male counterparts. First, they seem to have a greater knowledge of the local flora. "Flora" isn't even a word I would ever use, but I heard a woman on the show say it once, and it made me want to sound smart, too. Walking through an open field, a male contestant might notice a pile of bear shit, pick it up in his hands, and remark, "Hmm, looks like a grizzly was here not five minutes ago." But women somehow have the ability to see a mountain of steaming shit, and resist the temptation to squeeze it in their fingertips. Instead, they'll grab at the various medicinal plants within arms' reach, as if they were pushing a cart through the produce section at Whole Foods.

"See this root," says one female contestant as she holds it before her camera. "I can grind it with some moss to make a poultice to treat this infection." She then holds up her other hand, where a barbed fishhook has been stuck in her palm for two days.

"She's got a hook in her hand!" I scream. It takes every survival instinct I have to keep from throwing up.

"Quick, Lola, bring me a trash can. I don't want to puke onto my snuggle blanket!" But Lola can't hear me now. She left a few minutes ago to use the bathroom and never came back. I can hear her on the phone, talking to a friend.

The women on *Alone* just seem mentally tougher than the men. Certainly tougher than I've ever been. They tend to complain a lot less in the face of desperation. Personally, I don't get it. If you're stranded in the woods, what else are you going to do besides complain? And who are you annoying, anyway?

"You're missing the best part, Lola!" I call off.

I don't like the way the men on this show build shelters. Some of them live like animals, sleeping inside a pile of dead leaves, sharing a bed with worms and spiders. I've seen women, on the other hand, build log cabins, complete with driftwood furniture and tapestries made from animal skins. One woman constructed a sweat lodge. Can you imagine slowly starving to death, yet mustering enough energy to maintain that level of civility? To Lola, I'm always quick to point out how strong and impressive the women are because I think they make good role models. In a few months, my daughter will be out of the house and surviving on her own. I know that my job of raising her is coming to an end. It's good that she sees women like this. They can show her what strength looks like in a way I couldn't possibly. Of course, they look like they haven't bathed in months. They must smell horrible. I pull my shirt over my nose, just in case their stench seeps through the cable lines and into our living room. I can't believe my baby girl isn't a child anymore. How did this day sneak up on me? I should've surrounded our home with some old tin cans tied to fishing wire. I've seen it work against wolverines.

The show is over, and the living room is quiet now. Rather than sit in the stillness, I turn the channel to a program called *Tidying Up with Marie Kondo.* She's a Japanese organizing consultant who helps people remove clutter from their lives. Even though she barely speaks English, she has a delightful energy that can be understood in any language. I haven't verified this, but judging by the way she flits about, I estimate that Marie is no bigger than my thumbnail. You could probably keep three Marie Kondos in your breast pocket and still have room for a can of beer.

"Do you want to watch Marie Kondo with me?" I shout. "She's really good!" No answer.

Most of the homes she cleans are jam-packed with excessive furniture and shelves full of junk. Despite this, Marie approaches each house with such reverence. If it were me, I'd bark from the cab of a crane, "We're getting rid of all your worthless crap," then let loose with a wrecking ball. But not Marie Kondo. Before getting to work, she spends a few moments in each home, just sitting on the floor, silently holding space. Before I became a parent, this part would have made my eyes roll. But I'm less cynical now, more easily wounded, I suppose, so instead my eyes tear up. It's easy to see it as a houseful of clutter and garbage, but Marie recognizes these things for what they are. Memories. Instinctively, I reach over to touch my daughter's hand, but she left long ago.

"Does this spark joy?" Marie asks the homeowner, who has a kitchen cluttered with items. Invariably, that question will give the person pause. She'll describe the circumstances by which she obtained the object. Maybe she inherited it from her mother when she passed away.

"It was her dying wish that I have this," she might respond.

"But does it spark joy?" Marie asks again.

The answer is no, and Marie thanks the object, then gently places it in the donation pile, and I want to cry again. Imagine thanking an object for the contribution it made to your life. I've never once thought of doing that.

When Marie Kondo has finished her magic, the homeowners have a new attitude on life, enjoying empty spaces in their homes for the first time in years. They'll probably fill it back up in a matter of weeks, but for now, there's space. They thank Marie for restoring their lives, then she says a few words in Japanese and flies back to her home inside of an acorn. The whole process is so beautiful, so respectful. As the credits role, I peacefully consider my life, then bark at Cynthia, "We're throwing out all our shit!"

For the next several days, I'm on a mission to toss anything that doesn't spark joy. Goodbye, fourth-favorite sweater I barely wore. Goodbye, box of outdated electrical equipment that never had a chance to come in handy. So long, jeans that no longer fit me. The more I let go of things, the freer I feel. Or so I tell myself. I check the kitchen.

"Does this spark joy?" I ask Cynthia while dangling an old oven mitt.

"Actually, it sparks fear," she replies. "Look at the hole in the fingers." She's right. That is pretty terrifying. A properly functioning oven mitt doesn't seem like something one should skimp on. I put it in the trash.

I then move to the shelves in the living room, tossing out books I haven't touched in years but somehow thought defined who I was. There's an anthology of poems I read when I was in college, and even then, it was only to pass an exam. But if people don't see it on my bookshelf, how will they know I'm smart? I place it in a box, deciding that when it comes to my intelligence, I'll just keep people guessing.

"You no longer spark joy!" I tell a book on the subject of drought-tolerant plants. Once again, I'm a Roman emperor condemning prisoners to death. I toss it into a milk crate, then gently add, "But thank you."

As the day wears on, my mission becomes feverish. I'm possessed with getting rid of possessions.

"I don't need this ... I don't need this ... And why did I ever think I needed this!" Purging has taken hold of me, and it's too strong to shake. In less than a week, I've reduced my belongings by almost half. It's a lot, but I still have this nagging feeling that I can get rid of even more. I guess part of me thought I could narrow my things down to 10 survival items.

"Maybe I'm being too hard on myself," I think. "It's good to have more than one bar of soap."

Standing in the living room, I take in my work. The house feels emptier, and that's what I need right now. I'm middle-aged, and the emptiness makes our home feel full of possibility, as opposed to being full of choices already made. I convince myself there's an optimism to it.

Lola comes out from her bedroom, having just completed another college application, and stares at the massive pile waiting to be donated.

"What's gotten into you?" She smiles broadly, lighting up the room. I'm not entirely sure, but in a moment, I'll realize what it is.

"Do you want to watch *Alone* with me? It'll be fun!"

"Sorry," she says, bouncing out to meet her friends. The room grows dim again, and the sound of the shutting door echoes through our home. In her place she leaves more emptiness. I stare at the spot Lola was in, not two seconds ago. I can still see her beautiful green eyes, the ones that took my heart the day she was born.

"It's going to be okay," I tell myself. "Now there's more room for possibility."

"But how will I survive without her?" I cry. "When all she sparked was joy."

Le Flâneur

How long should a dog sniff a fire hydrant before it's time to worry? Five minutes? Ten minutes? Ours could spend an entire afternoon sniffing the one at the end of the street. That urine-soaked fire hydrant was like an all-you-can-smell buffet, and she simply didn't have the willpower to exercise portion control.

"Save some stink for the next animal!" I'd tell her. She was greedy that way, stuffing her snout with enough smells to fill a rented bowling shoe. I was embarrassed about it. When people passed us standing at that hydrant for so long, I looked at them apologetically and offered, "She's a rescue," just so they'd understand that it was the previous owner who had failed her, and not me. I had to make that clear, because isn't that what neighbors do when they meet? Judge each other?

Because these sniffing marathons took forever, Cynthia and I would walk our dog together. This way, we could entertain each other while our dog took a smell and then left a smell, like it was the penny tray at a convenience store. It became our daily activity, and I used that time to unload all my problems on Cynthia. Sometimes, it was about the struggles I had in my career, but just as often she'd help me better understand my parents or my children. She's really good at stuff like that. When our dog died, we no longer had those moments, and the worry in my stomach had no place to go.

"We can still take evening walks," Cynthia suggested, a few days after we received the ashes of our pet. They taped a photo of our dog to the lid so that one day, far in the future, we wouldn't find a mysterious box, wonder what was inside, then react in horror. Cynthia's idea of taking walks together surprised me. It seemed obvious, but also preposterous ... like, if you saw it in a movie, you'd roll your eyes and say, "Yeah, we're really supposed to believe a couple that's been married for 20 years would go on walks together if there wasn't a dog pulling them."

I agreed to her suggestion, even though I couldn't imagine we'd actually hold ourselves to it. It was just easier not to. But surprisingly, day after day, we'd take our evening walk. On days that Cynthia worked later than I did, I'd wait impatiently at the door for her to arrive, just like our dog did.

"Hurry up and get changed," I wagged in excitement.

At first, we walked only around the block, retracing our familiar steps, loitering at the spots our dog enjoyed so much. Soon, we were exploring farther and farther.

Ours is a middle-class neighborhood, and architecturally speaking, the houses aren't very interesting. Most are simple, postwar boxes that were built for returning soldiers. Thanks to the exploding real-estate market, today, these small, unimpressive homes are likely to have a luxury car parked in the driveway. Some are built into the hillside, so that the garage is at street level, and the bedrooms are underneath, hugging the mountain. This way, when an earthquake strikes in the middle of the night, the occupants don't have to worry about finding their car. It'll be on their heads.

I think it's the plainness of these homes that compels their owners to make a statement with their front yards. It says, "Don't judge me by my house, which I played no part in creating. Judge me by my front yard, which I ruined all by myself." And so I oblige and judge them.

One homeowner decided to rip up his lawn and replace it with a sea of white gravel. It makes their yard look like the bottom of a fish tank, even if it lacks a treasure chest that pops open every few seconds. I never noticed stuff like this when I used to drive by. But on foot, the offenses are obvious and unforgivable.

Another neighbor must think she's a character in a fairy tale. I say this because of the wishing well stationed beneath her magnolia tree. It's made of faux wood, and a handful of ceramic bunnies are scattered in its shadow. Real bunnies are skittish and would never hang around that long, but these bunnies hold still—frozen in humiliation. I once dropped a nickel into her well, hoping my wish might come true, but the next day the well was still there. Anyway, there really is a lot to judge on these walks, if you're willing to put in the work. And I am.

At first, judging like this was just a guilty pleasure of mine. But when I learned that other people also do it, and that there's actually a word to describe it, I grew more comfortable. It's called *flâneuring*. The term was popularized in the 19th century by the French poet Baudelaire. I couldn't tell you much about Baudelaire, other than that his name sounds snooty, but in truth, that's all you need to know. A *flâneur* is someone who strolls around his neighborhood, critically observing other people's lives. He holds his nose high in the air, and his derision lingers, leaving a trail of condescension, like dog piss on a telephone pole. I was born to *flâneur*.

One Saturday morning, Cynthia and I opted for a change of scenery. Rather than walk the same route, we got in the car and drove to an upscale neighborhood a few miles from us called La Cañada. In La Cañada, the weather is always nicer, by virtue of their higher property taxes. The clouds just seem puffier, and if you have the extra 300K, it's well worth the money. It seemed bold to drive to someone else's neighborhood just to walk around —almost like trespassing. "Just who do you think you are?" I expected someone to say. To pre-empt that, I wore an old Princeton T-shirt, so that the locals would think I was someone who practices law instead of disdain. We parked the car, and Cynthia opened Google Maps on her phone. She dropped a pin so we could find our way back, and off we went like Hansel and Gretel.

The T-shirt served its purpose because, within a few minutes, we passed a woman jogging, and she waved like we were neighbors whose names she had simply forgotten. I waved back, as if to say, "Thanks for taking in our mail, Stacy." It felt good to be mistaken for one of their own. It made me feel like I could be rich, like them, if only I had made a few different choices in life.

In the distance, the faint sound of a brook could be heard as it wound its way between houses. This may not seem like a big deal, but it rarely rains in Southern California, so the sound of flowing water is miraculous. And to have it within earshot of your bedroom—could there be anything better? We ambled for a while, enjoying the chatter of the stream as it tumbled down the hillside, tripping over every rock in its path. In the next town to the south, our town, the stream would be diverted underground into a drainage pipe, where it would eventually dump into the sea. In Los Angeles, water is treated as garbage. In this neighborhood, at least, it was heralded like music.

There was one home, a beautiful Gothic Revival from the 1920s, that reminded me of Wayne Manor, from the old *Batman* TV series. It was enormous, and it filled me with both judgment and resentment. "No one should have this much money!" followed by "Why don't *I* have this much money?!"

"Because you chose to lead a creative life," responded Cynthia. I was in no mood for a history lesson.

"They must have more bedrooms than beds," I continued. "And if that's the case, they don't even know how to use them. A bedroom needs a bed. It's not a special place for you to wrap gifts." That's the thing. If you want to feel better about your station in life, you have to know how to turn someone else's positive into a negative.

Our house, for example, has the same number of beds as bedrooms. I take pride knowing that I have the perfect bed-to-bedroom ratio. There's no way that was the case with this giant mansion. It would need more beds than a Sit 'n Sleep showroom. The swing set in the backyard also did a number on me. The slide looked bright green, not yet faded by the sun, and the ropes were clean and new. It was obvious that the owners had a young child, which probably made them younger than me.

"How are they able to afford all this?" I asked Cynthia. But what I was really asking was, "How are they so much more successful than me?"

"They're probably both professionals. Like, investment bankers or corporate attorneys."

"Yeah, you're right. They must hate their jobs."

That's what makes *flâneuring* such a satisfying pastime. You can judge someone and come to whatever verdict you feel like reaching. It's sublime, really.

"They probably don't hate their jobs," Cynthia corrected me. "People who hate their jobs don't do them well, and you have to in order to make his kind of money."

Cynthia's not as good at *flâneuring* as I am.

The following weekend, we found ourselves walking in a

fancy neighborhood in Pasadena. It was down by the *arroyo,* which is the word Southern Californians use to describe a concrete channel that used to be a river. Anywhere else, people would say, "Down by the dry, shitty river," but here, it's an *arroyo* —so enticing and romantic. It was a summer morning, and we had gotten up early to avoid the harsh sunshine. In Los Angeles, something happens when the sun gets high. The sky begins to buzz with a hazy-white glow. It's no different than being stuck inside a fluorescent tube. People talk about the lack of sunshine causing seasonal affective disorder, but to me the opposite is just as true. I can't stand the blinding sunshine, so instead I become a vampire, avoiding direct contact with the sun's rays. When we walk, I insist on crisscrossing the street to whichever side offers more shade. It was during one of these crisscrosses that we noticed a crowd of cars farther ahead, vying for parking spots. A sign on the corner read: ESTATE SALE. My dog would've loved to piss on it.

"We should go in!" said Cynthia.

Garage sales aren't my thing. Neither are rummage sales, yard sales, or tag sales. It's not treasure, it's junk that people no longer need, but instead of donating it or paying to have it hauled away, they expect us to buy it from them. "If you like garbage, then I've got a deal for you!" Estate sales are slightly different. These are people who kept their clutter problems to themselves, died, then made it the problem of their next of kin. Like the other homes in this neighborhood, this one was old and grand. There was ivy climbing the walls, and a long U-shaped driveway invited you to the front door before curving away, reminding you to leave.

"It'll be fun!" shouted Cynthia, bounding ahead.

We approached, passing beneath the arch of a giant wrought-iron gate, which ordinarily must have been locked. A woman greeted us at the front door.

"Come on in, y'all," she belted, with the kind of smile you only see on people who are trying to sell you something. The bright-red apron across her chest confirmed this: KLD ESTATE LIQUIDATORS.

I dawdled outside for a bit, surprised that after having spent so much time speculating about the lives of the rich, I didn't want confirmation. It seemed to take away the sport of it.

"Right this way," instructed the woman in the apron. That sounded more like a command than an invitation, and I felt compelled to comply. I can't imagine the actual owner ever greeted their guests this way, but that didn't matter. The house belonged to the liquidators now.

Normally, you don't just barge into someone's home—especially a home as grand as this. There's a ritual pause—a moment at the threshold where you wipe the crud off your shoes on the doormat, even if only symbolically, then you enter cautiously and respectfully. That moment was no longer required. Most everyone just rushed in without hesitating. A few slowed down once they hit the foyer, but only in the way one does at a supermarket, unsure which way the shampoo aisle is.

The air inside was thin and stale and the front hallway, once imposing, was now set up like a flea market. Crystal candy dishes and serving bowls were arranged on card tables, and jewelry was displayed in glass cases that were brought in for the occasion. The only thing missing was a cart selling churros.

According to the woman working the cashbox, an elderly couple lived here, but the wife had recently passed, and now the husband was selling everything. Assisted living was his next stop, and after that, un-assisted un-living. To everyone's great luck, the couple's entire life was now available for purchase, and at a steep discount.

"Shouldn't we have a moment of silence?" I thought of saying as the vultures picked through their remains. Instead of silence, *AM Gold* played on a hi-fi system from the 1970s, which was also for sale. "Midnight at the Oasis." I checked my watch and then my surroundings. It was neither midnight nor an oasis of any kind.

To avoid the crowd in the main hallway, I ducked into the first open room. It was a library with mahogany built-ins, but given the fanciness of this house, it could've just as easily been called a "parlour" and spelled with a *u*. The entire rear wall was dedicated to rows of dusty, old books. Most looked like they hadn't been read in years. That's the problem with buying books—people feel compelled to keep them. What are you supposed to do with a book after you've read it? It feels shameful to throw it away, even though you're unlikely to read it again. So instead, you just stash it on a shelf, like a memory you plan to revisit one day but never get around to.

Another wall had several volumes of expensive, leather-bound books—the kind that people call handsome when they're itching to sound pretentious. Unlike their paperback cousins that had been read once and put away, these books looked like they'd never been read at all. They were props, yet, despite that, were given luxury seats, staring at the Himalayas on the giant and handsome floor globe. Splayed on a nearby table were boxes and boxes of high-end personal stationery. Each one represented a new time period with an updated font. Most of the paper was textured, so that it almost resembled fabric. If the pieces were larger, you could've sewed a coat out of them. As I stared at all this blank stationery, I couldn't help but think of the hundreds of invitations, condolences, and thank-you letters that were never sent. It was a lifetime of things left unsaid. What really struck me was that the sender's name wasn't embossed on the stationery. Instead, the address was written—as if the letters were sent from the house itself. The house, it must've seemed to the occupants, was the important part.

As I walked down the hall, I noticed that my hands were now clasped behind my back. It's not how I usually carry myself, so regal and uptight, like I'm scoring a baking competition. But I was holding my hands like that to keep from actually touching things. It seemed so disrespectful, especially when I saw other people doing it. The grabbiest ones were the antique dealers and swap-meet vendors, looking for treasure to flip. I didn't know how to act, so I looked around for guidance—someone who could show me how to poke my way through a stranger's life while still being considerate. There wasn't anyone like that in the sunroom. Maybe I should check the butler's pantry.

There I found a small elevator. Even though it probably hadn't functioned in decades, it's hard not to be impressed by a mansion that has an elevator. By the way I reacted to it, you would think that I'd never seen an elevator before. "You mean this magic box can carry you from the basement to the attic?"

Because it was out of use, it was filled with a mountain of possessions that this family had collected over the years: copper pots, every *National Geographic* magazine from 1962 to 1978, empty cookie tins, and boxes of holiday decorations. They had so much stuff they didn't need. And what better place to store it all than inside something else you don't need. It was a Russian nestling doll of garbage. How could they accumulate so many things, and worse still, keep them for a lifetime? Maybe they decided that all of it was important to them. But if everything is important, then isn't nothing important?

I was mad at the owners now. What bothered me the most was that they had put themselves in a position where their entire lives lay exposed for people to sift through. Strangers would pick up an antique clock or porcelain figurine, handle it for a few seconds, then set it back down as if to say, "Nah, it may have been good enough for you, but not for me." It's just so offensive.

I ventured up the grand staircase, where each step showcased a different pair of women's shoes. Most seemed to be for formal occasions, and going by their styles, they easily spanned several decades. It was creepy how they just stood there, footless, waiting to be ridden to the ball.

Upstairs, where the bedrooms were, I passed a closed door with a sign that read: DO NOT ENTER. A young woman with dark sunglasses hanging from the neck of her T-shirt tried anyway. She turned the knob clockwise, then counterclockwise, giving the door a good shove each time. It wouldn't budge, so she gave up and continued toward the main bedroom. There was a man, probably someone she didn't know, following a few steps behind. Even though he saw her try to open the door, he still tested the lock for himself. This actually upset me. With the dozens of open rooms in this house, and the thousands of items that were for sale, this was the one small area that was off limits, and they couldn't honor that. Behind this closed door were the things of most importance, I realized. The private items that weren't for sale. Everyone needed to know what they were, as if this room contained the secret to life. A half-hour ago, I would've been curious, too, but I had since changed my mind.

"Do we have to see every fucking detail of their existence?!" I wanted to scream as I retreated back down the staircase, past the shoes that were frozen in time.

The chatter at the front door was loud now, and disco music pushed its way out from the decaying speakers. I spotted Cynthia standing at the cashier's box.

"I'll be at the curb," I mouthed, and she nodded.

Outside, the traffic was getting thicker as the swarms arrived, all jockeying for spots on the street. I sat on the curb angrily as the hot cement baked me from the outside. My mood had soured from all the judging—mine and everyone else's. That's the thing about *flâneuring*—it's safer if you don't get beyond the front door, where the truth is kept.

A few minutes later, Cynthia found me. She was holding a vintage, red umbrella, with a long, elegant stem. It probably hadn't been opened since the 1950s.

"Why did you have to buy their shit?" Now I was mad at her for being one of scavengers.

"I like it," she said, waving me over.

Annoyed, I arose and brushed the dirt from my shorts. Cynthia turned on her cell phone and opened the map. Our car was a few miles away, across the bridge, on the other side of the *arroyo.* It was a long walk, and with the overhead sun beating down on us, it would feel even farther.

"We shouldn't have gone inside," I barked, my eyes squinting from the brightness. "It's a thousand fucking degrees, and now I've gotta lug this shit home with me, to keep until the day that I die? And for what purpose? It doesn't even rain here!"

"I know." Cynthia smiled softly. Then she pulled on the stem, opening the canopy. "Come stand next to me."

I inched my way over, and things began to change. It was more bearable here, beneath the shadow of a stranger's red umbrella. The light was kinder. I huddled at Cynthia's side, our shoulders just barely touching, as we plotted a course back to our lives.

A Plague upon Your House

I took Lola to the East Coast to tour colleges. Cynthia had already done the same with Roxy, and this was to be my turn. One final trip with my baby before she belonged to the world. The script called for us to visit eight colleges in five days, and even though she wasn't coming with us, Cynthia mapped out the whole thing. Where to stay, where to park, who to meet with, and when to leave for the next college. I was grateful for her help. The logistics of planning such a trip are overwhelming for me. Too many moving parts, and so many things that can go wrong.

Lola was worried that I would spoil the trip by being my naturally over-anxious self, but she was wrong. I didn't wait until the trip started. The day before we left, I checked Waze to estimate how long it would take to get from our house to the airport. Then I added an extra half-hour, just in case. Then I added an extra half-hour on top of that—just in case, just in case. The next morning, I waited impatiently by the front door while Lola was taking her time eating breakfast. It wasn't time to leave yet, but I was annoyed that she wasn't acting like we had a plane to catch, when we literally had a plane to catch.

"Seriously, Lola? Would you like to look at the dessert menu?"

"We have time, Dad! Don't stress me out!"

Unfortunately for them, my kids picked the wrong father for that. For the most part, I live constantly on edge. Although the trip went off without a hitch, it's hard to know if that was because of me or in spite of me.

Months later, Lola accepted admission to a great school. They don't advertise this on the website, but they have a campus in my house. It's located down the hallway from the kitchen, in my daughter's bedroom. Thanks to the COVID-19 pandemic, that's what her first year of college looked like.

When I was her age, I wasn't living in a pandemic, but I did study them. As an undergraduate, I took a class called "The History of Plagues." It turned out to be one of my favorite classes, and initially I wasn't even sure if I wanted to take it. Navigating my field of study was so daunting, I often relied on the course reviews so that someone else could make the decision for me. "What does everyone here think I should study?" They kept a book of these reviews in the registrar's office, and it was always a fun read. In the case of this class, the student reviews were glowing. "A wild ride for the whole family," wrote one student. "Leave mom at home and bring a date," wrote another. But it was the one that described the lecture on tuberculosis as "a breath of fresh air" that pushed me over the top.

The class convened in a modern lecture hall with tiered seating, like a movie theater. Undeniably, this added to the theatricality of the course, but most of the credit went to its unlikely star, the professor who taught it. He was a middle-aged man, slight in stature. Not exactly a leading man—he was more of a character actor. His black, wiry hair spilled from beneath the Scottish paddy cap he seemed absolutely committed to wearing. It couldn't have been easy to look at himself in the mirror like that, but the man knew what his audience wanted, and he didn't disappoint. He reminded me of Gallagher, the prop comedian who used to smash watermelons with a sledgehammer. Seen through the lens of his humorous lectures, the various plagues that decimated Europe were more amusing than they were terrifying.

Throughout the course, the professor promised that, in an upcoming lecture, he would drop a knowledge bomb so explosive it would alter the way we looked at disease. It was a brilliant move because it scared us into never missing a class. Some days he'd almost tell us, then pause.

"No, not today. You'll have to wait." And the class would groan. This guy knew how to work the room. If there was an open guitar case for tips, I would've considered leaving something.

On the last day of the semester, he thanked us for signing up for his class, wished us luck on the final, then dismissed us.

"Wait!" shouted the mob. "You never told us about the disease!"

"Ah, right you are."

He backtracked from the door and returned to the lectern, removing his scarf as he sat on the table at the front of the class. The move was unnecessarily melodramatic, which is exactly how I would've played it.

"Okay," he said. "What's the only disease in history that, if left untreated, is 100 percent fatal?"

"AIDS," shouted a kid leaning against the wall.

"Nope."

"Bubonic plague," shouted another.

"Wrong."

An awkward-looking kid screamed, "Syphilis!" He had to be a virgin, so I don't know what he was worried about. Also not it.

The professor paused, milking the moment. His eyes scanned

our faces, documenting how we were before this revelation, and how we would be afterward. Forever changed.

"The only disease that is 100 percent fatal if left untreated is ... rabies."

The room let out a collective gasp. "Rabies!" We were stunned, I think, because rabies is so pedestrian. There's nothing foreign or remote about it. It was something you could run out and get in a few hours, like a scratcher card from 7-Eleven. All you had to do was pet a stray dog, wait for the crazy little fucker to tear off your thumb, and in a few hours you'd be shopping for tombstones.

"I'm sorry, sir. Did you say 'granite' or 'marble'? It's hard to understand you through the foaming."

After the course ended, plague was one of the few things I didn't worry about. It was reserved for history, when people cured ailments with magic spells. Our society would never befall the same fate. We had modern science and common sense. Yet here I was, 10 months after the COVID-19 pandemic first struck the United States, hiding beneath my bed.

Not to brag, but I was among the first to panic. I'd been tracking the virus since it appeared in China, anxiously waiting for it to hit our shores, like atomic radiation carried on the wind.

Preparing for the worst has long been a guilty pleasure of mine. As a child, I slept in a sleeping bag every night. It was brown and torn at the bottom, allowing my toes to dip into the stuffing. As soon as the lights were off, I'd crawl deep inside, pulling the top over my head, then I'd press the buttons of an imaginary computer that I guess was sewn into the fabric. This would activate a force field that would protect me in my sleep. Then I'd hit the buttons some more, activating a force field for the force field. Just in case, just in case. All this was to protect me—the most important person on the planet.

Twentysomething years later, I lost that title to my first daughter, Roxy. It began when Cynthia was pregnant. I would sing into her belly because someone told me that's what I was supposed to do. I'm terrible with music lyrics, so it was the same Louis Prima song every day for months. When Roxy was finally born, she came out screaming and crying. They say newborns do that to clear their lungs, but to me she just seemed so scared. I picked her up, and even though she was wailing so loudly that it hurt my ears, I sang to her just above a whisper.

Almost instantly, my baby stopped crying and just stared at me. My daughter recognized me, and I was so touched by that. I held her in my arms, but with her soft, blue eyes, *she* held *me*. I'm not a religious person at all, but in that moment I was hit by the divine.

"This is what God looks like," I thought. "I'm looking at God."

And then I did exactly what billions of parents before me have been genetically programed to do. I surrendered to my child. I was no longer the most important person on the planet. I became a worker drone, protecting the queen with his life.

She was only a few minutes old when a nurse tried to take her from me. She wanted to put my baby in one of those clear, plastic bins—the kind that looks like it should pass through the X-ray machine at the airport. It caught me by surprise.

"Is there something wrong with my daughter?

"No. She looks perfectly healthy."

"But you want to put her in that thing?"

"We do it with all the babies."

"Fuck no," I said. "I'm not letting her out of my sight."

At home, I child-proofed every door, latch, and lid so that even a safecracker couldn't get through them. Grabbing a bar of soap from under the sink was like the plotline of *Ocean's Eleven.*

And this was to prevent the dangers coming from inside my own home. Imagine how I felt about the outside dangers. Forget shopping for blankies and stuffed animals—I stocked up on survival gear. For earthquakes, I bought water-purifying tablets, solar generators, and freeze-dried food. And for evacuation due to wildfires, I stuffed my kid's clothes in "go bags" hidden in our cars.

"These are smoke hoods," I told my daughters when they were little. I put them in their nightstands. "You're never, ever going to need them. Probably. If there's a fire in the house, you put these on and crawl to safety." Of course this scared them, but I had two queens now, Roxy and Lola, and they both needed to be protected—whatever the cost. To me or them.

As unlikely as it sounds, I was even prepared for the pandemic. In one of the emergency bins stashed in my garage, I had two unopened boxes of surgical masks. And not the cheap stuff. I had N95s—the kind hospitals couldn't get their hands on. At one point, this was just me being a responsible adult. But somehow, like the coronavirus, it mutated into something more sinister. It was no longer about being prepared for the outside world. It was about keeping the chaos inside me at bay.

This chaos always had a way of spilling out whenever I was stressed. If I was between jobs, I told my children we were spending too much money. If the stove was on, no matter where they were, I told them they were standing too close. Actually, it didn't even matter what I said, it was the way I said it. Not with tenderness, the way you'd talk to a loved one, but with panic, to convey the horror of every possibility.

"The virus is coming," I announced while reading the news one winter morning, "And we're all fucked."

At the time, Lola was enrolled in an all-girls school called Immaculate Heart. We're Jewish, but I liked the school because of its strong academic reputation, even if I did have to look the other way every time I passed the Virgin Mary statue. In fairness, she did the same for me, keeping her gaze affixed to the baby she was cradling in her arms. What was his name? Anyway, we had a mutual understanding, me and V.M.

As far as parents went, I wasn't exactly a fixture on campus, but I did know my way around. A few months earlier, during a scorching heat wave, I had to bring my tuition bill to the front office. The moment I stepped out of the car, I could feel the hot air pulling the moisture out of my body like one of those vacuum bags you seal old sweaters in. It was grotesque, and my limbs wilted in protest as I lumbered across the softball field.

When I finally made it to the front office, I slammed the door behind me like it was the air lock to the Space Station, threw my body against the counter, and glared at the administrator.

"Is it 115 degrees outside, or am I just a Jew picking up his daughter from Catholic school?"

But this time, on the eve of the pandemic lockdown, with the media screaming about a virus that would literally take our breath away, I was in no mood for sacrilegious pleasantries.

"Look, we've had a good run," I said to the administrator. "But I'm pulling my daughter out. And it has nothing to do with me being Jewish and you being Catholic ... even if I do feel compelled to bring it up every time we see each other."

"I know you're concerned about COVID," she responded, "But I want to assure you—"

"Nope," I interrupted. "We shouldn't even be sharing the same air. We can do this over the phone. If I'm not in, the principal can leave me a V.M."

I crossed to the door, then stopped myself.

"That stands for 'voicemail,' not 'Virgin Mary.'"

As we drove away, my cell phone buzzed with an emergency notification. The school was switching to remote learning.

"For, like, a few weeks?" asked Lola.

I suppose I could've found a delicate way to break the news to her, to shield her from the scary truth. But instead I blurted, "A few weeks? Fuck, it's going to be way longer than that, honey. This is a nightmare." And now she was scared, too.

When we got home, I locked the front door and fell back into my comfortable role.

"Go to the bathroom and wash your hands," I told her. "I'll take care of everything else."

I wiped the house down. The doorknobs, the faucets, the handles, the counters ... anything that could've been touched in the past 12 months. This was upon the advice of a doctor I discovered on YouTube. He shared his routine on how to sterilize groceries, as if they were surgical instruments. Here I am scrubbing the shopping bag. Here I am scrubbing the bag inside the bag. Here I am scrubbing my hands after it held the bag inside the bag. This guy was absolutely nuts, and I found his level of obsessive compulsion to be aspirational. I was almost giddy watching it. When my frantic, hour-long tongue bath was finally complete, I set down the wipes and reflected upon my work. Lola was safe now.

Getting Roxy home was harder. She was in Florida with a friend, having been invited there for Spring Break. That night, I began to worry that the government might shut down the flights. Having a daughter stranded during a pandemic was one of the few things I hadn't prepared for. How did I leave that off my checklist when I stored sneakers in my car in case I needed to run to my daughters' school after an earthquake? That was the plan, by the way. I told them this when they were in grade school. In the event of an earthquake, they should stay where they were. The roads might be down, but I had an emergency backpack in my car and I would run to them. Even if it took me five hours, I would protect them because they're everything to me.

Maybe I could drive to Florida and pick Roxy up. But it's a five-day trip. How could I safely stop?

Despite living in a constant state of readiness, I'm not the guy you want to know in an emergency. I panic too easily. I become blind with fear—reptilian, almost, relying on my base instincts and licking my eyeballs in an attempt to see clearly. Cynthia knows this about me, so she takes charge, freeing me up to do what I do best: catastrophize.

Roxy was panicking, too. Not some ordinary hand-wringing —she was having a legitimate panic attack. Was it even safe to get on a plane? Would she get sick? Who would care for her?

"Put her on the next available flight home," I screamed. "Whatever it costs."

This was me and Roxy in disaster mode—disasters.

A few years earlier, Cynthia enrolled Roxy in a self-defense class. The course was just for women, and Roxy was among the youngest there, just a high-school kid, but Cynthia insisted this couldn't wait any longer. She was right. Our daughter had been leaving the house more, hanging out in public, and wandering farther and farther from my watchful eye.

The course lasted several weekends, and for the graduation ceremony, family members were invited to watch their loved ones fight in a simulated attack. I got there early and found a seat a few feet away from the padded floor. As I waited for everyone to file in, I leafed through one of the brochures left on the front counter. The women in the photos looked bold and empowered, but maybe due to the high gloss of the paper, they didn't seem real.

When it was time, the instructor took to the mat and gave the audience a rundown of what the students had been taught. It was street fighting, and the women were trained to use whatever means necessary to level the playing field. He warned us that watching this exhibition would be ugly and visceral, because it was intended to mirror real life. I braced myself. I'm not really good at drawing boundaries like that. Even when watching an upsetting movie, I have to remind myself that none of it's real. They're just actors playing a role written by a screenwriter like me.

A man came to the center of the mat. He was to play the part of the attacker, and was covered head to toe in thick padding. It made him look friendly, like the Michelin Man, promising to give your car a more pleasant ride. For a moment, that put me at ease. Maybe this wouldn't be so bad after all.

One by one, women were called up to fight, showcasing their various defense tactics. It was impressive, but like the brochure I had just read, it felt distant. Nothing more than a demonstration of skill. Then it was my daughter's turn. I applauded loudly when she took the mat, the way I did at her middle-school play, back when she wore overalls every day. I beamed with pride as she steeled herself for battle. Within seconds, all that changed.

The man charged at her, grabbing her as she frantically punched the mask covering his face.

"Help! Call 911!" she screamed, and he threw her to the mat, violently.

"Hold still, you bitch!" he yelled. This to my baby. And I gasped. He was assaulting her. This didn't look like a demonstration at all. This looked real. I mean, was I the only one seeing this? And why wasn't anyone helping her? My heart was pounding against my chest, trying to leap out of my body to do something.

"This is just a simulation," I reminded myself as my hands gripped the bench, keeping me from running to her side. The man was on top of her, pinning her to the mat, and she was fighting back but losing. She was tiny, maybe a third of his size.

My breath was shallow and fast, and I was having trouble seeing through the tears welling in my eyes.

"I need to save her!"

I was panicking now. The man in the padding was doing a good and necessary thing, but I couldn't recognize that. I wanted to break his neck. I wanted to gouge his eyes out with my fingers, digging deep into his skull until I pulled out his fucking soul.

Desperately, Roxy squirmed to get out from under him, punching and thrashing, screaming louder and louder.

Now my feet were trembling, urging the rest of me to get up and protect my child, instead of just sitting there—failing her.

Finally, she freed herself, called for help, and the attack was called off. The instructor commended her, and the class applauded. But at that point, the damage was done to me. I was frozen, and I felt like vomiting.

Despite the pandemic, we managed to get Roxy safely home from Florida. We broke the news to her about what her future might look like, and she went off the rails.

"I'll never get to go to college! This is so unfair!" she cried.

This is her at her most anxious, when her mind races to the worst possible conclusion of every scenario. Her brain boils over, erupting like a volcano as it spews her worries until there's nothing left inside her. It's a burden she inherited from me, and it was so upsetting to hear that I had to leave the room.

I was at the dining-room table, scouring the Internet for more bad news about the pandemic, when she finally calmed down. I overheard her talking to Cynthia. I don't know what they were saying, and I only caught the tail end. But what I heard was enough to make the façade that I had created for myself come tumbling down.

"Don't bring Dad into this," she said. "He'll only make me feel worse."

It's strange how hard that hit me, given that she had said those exact words to my face countless times before. Usually it was in response to some warning I was giving her. I'd lay out the potential dangers, then she'd bark, "I know, Dad. You don't need to scare me!"

I always thought this was just Roxy's way of dismissing me. A know-it-all teenager trying to shut her father up. But when I heard her say it behind my back, she wasn't saying it to hurt me. She was saying it because it was true. That's when I finally heard her—when I wasn't supposed to.

All these years, I thought I was protecting my daughters. But in reality, I was just terrifying them. My worries were too much for me to handle on my own, so I shared them with my children. My own children. It's the most selfish thing I've ever done. During the quiet hours of the night, it chokes me with shame until the tears come.

Not far from us there's a country road, a few miles long, that winds up a mountain. It dead-ends at a public golf course, so few cars travel on it. But the ones that do do so at dangerously fast speeds. I used to run on it during the weekends, but I could never really enjoy it. With the occasional car rounding blind corners at 60 m.p.h., I gave up and stuck to running on the trails, where I only had to worry about rattlesnakes. When the pandemic hit, the city shut down the golf course and locked the gate at the bottom of the hill, freeing the road of all traffic.

A placard hanging from the bars warned trespassers to keep away. I imagine that to others, the sight must've been foreboding. But that's not how I perceived it. Knowing that this road was now closed to cars, I read it like an invitation.

The gate was too difficult to climb, but toward the ground there was a small gap between it and the road. I slid through, wiped the gravel from my shorts, and took off running. The road was all mine, and I flaunted it by running right in the middle, on the double yellow line. The paint was thick and raised just a little, so you could actually feel it with your feet. About a mile up, the carob trees that adorned the street gave way to evergreens, and I spotted a pine cone on the road. A few weeks earlier, it wouldn't have lasted more than five minutes before being crushed beneath the wheels of a Range Rover. Yet here it was, lounging in the sun without a worry.

Weeds were beginning to sprout in the cracks of the asphalt, and the grasses near the curb were already starting to encroach. Given enough time, nature would reclaim even more of what was hers. For a landscape that looked eerily post-apocalyptic, I was surprised it didn't feel that way.

At the top of the mountain, the hilltops parted, releasing a view of downtown Los Angeles. When the governor declared a lockdown, cars were finally off the roads, taking with them enormous amounts of pollution. "Fine particulates" is what they call them, and they're cancerous. I've read all about them. You can wipe them off the window ledge like frosting on a cake. Almost overnight, the air in Southern California became completely unfamiliar. It became clean. The local news reported that, for three days in a row, Los Angeles had the freshest air in the country. Without the smog, I could see so clearly. I could make out the shapes and colors of buildings 20 miles away.

The air even felt different. It seemed thinner. So thin, actually, that it almost felt unsafe to breathe—like there wouldn't be enough oxygen in it. Imagine that being your first thought after breathing fresh air. Is this going to kill me? Initially, the pandemic had me worried out of my mind, but now, I wasn't thinking of

COVID. I was thinking of the plague inside me. I sat down in the middle of the road, right on the double yellow line, because how often can you do that? How often can you travel a road and not be afraid?

Despite having been promised the freedom of adulthood, the pandemic captured my daughters inside their bedrooms, where they paced and roared like caged lions. It was cruel for them, but maybe this was an opportunity for me. Maybe there would be enough time to change my behavior, and re-write the waning days of their youth. A chance at redemption, so that their final childhood memories of their father would be something other than the man who poisoned them with fear. Thanks to this awful pandemic, there was hope for me.

The morning sun was hitting the tall fountain grass from behind, making their furry tails glow as they swayed in the wind. Powered little engines they were, each stalk trying so hard to break free, only to be snapped back into place like a habit that can't be broken. In the distance, a city worker was mowing the golf course on a tractor. It filled the air with the sweet scent of freshly cut grass. It's unmistakeable. Someone once told me that the smell is actually pain, as the grass releases chemicals to heal itself. So that's what pain is for.

The groundskeeper was rounding the corner, and soon I'd be in his line of vision. I decided it was best to leave before he spotted me. I rose to my feet and jogged back down the hill, to my captive children on the other side of the gate. There was no rush now. For the foreseeable future, at least, I could protect them—from myself. And see so clearly. And breathe so deep.

Epilogue: Finding the Story

After performing my personal essays to live audiences, I host a talkback. It's basically me, sitting onstage, fielding whatever questions people have. This suggestion came from a friend who is a theater director, and at first, I had mixed feelings about it. I wanted the audience to leave the theater and sit in whatever they were feeling. I thought a talkback would get in the way of that. Nevertheless, he convinced me to give it a shot, and I soon realized that this conversation actually deepened the audience's experience, allowing them to further connect with the work. This epilogue is essentially a talkback on paper, and I hope it serves the same function for you.

I've been a professional television writer since 1996. My credits include *King of the Hill, Just Shoot Me, Beavis and Butt-Head, Wilfred, Maron, Rules of Engagement, Out of Practice, Brickleberry, Glenn Martin DDS, Tacoma FD,* and dozens of pilots and feature scripts. I've been fortunate enough to make a living at screenwriting, which is what I'd wanted to do ever since I was a teenager. Many people, however, are surprised to learn that, professionally speaking, I don't write what I want to write.

I write what people pay me to write, and sometimes the two are far apart. Additionally, screenwriting is very collaborative. We get notes from studio executives, producers, directors, actors, and other writers. Everyone has creative input, and compromises have to be made. Often this makes the work better, but it always makes it less "mine" and more "ours." All of this, I guess, began to weigh on me. I wanted to write something that was just mine.

One day, I shared this with my wife.

"I have a terrible idea," I said. "I'm thinking of writing a collection of personal essays. It would take me years to write, and even if I sold it, I probably wouldn't make any money."

"Oh my God," she responded. "You have to."

"Why? Why do I have to?" I was almost mad at her for supporting this idea. Writing is how I pay the bills. If I don't get paid for my work, what's the point?

"Because if you do," she responded, "You'll find yourself."

I guess it was obvious that I needed to find myself.

So began the task of learning how to write in a whole new genre. As a screenwriter, I create fictional characters and tell their stories. Because they're not real, I have the luxury of not worrying about hurting their feelings. I can say all sorts of awful things about them, and it's perfectly fine. With personal essays, however, I don't have that luxury. I'm real, the people in my life are real, and all of us have feelings. So how do I honor these real people with the grace and compassion that they deserve, and also make it entertaining?

This tension between fiction and nonfiction is why I find personal-essay writing to be so powerful. It's a piece of creative writing, but because the people are real, the stakes are higher. Writing this way was appealing to me, but I still didn't know how to actually do it. How was I supposed to take the smallest, almost forgotten moments of my life and weave them into something that felt like a story?

Writing for the first time without a boss or collaborator was both freeing and unsettling. If I was working on a television show, there would be a staff to help me. Before a word is ever written, a roomful of writers can easily spend a week figuring out how an idea unfolds into an episode. The emotional beats, the act breaks, the subplots ... everything is worked out in advance. This process is called "breaking a story," and it's how a story is invented.

But I couldn't invent my personal stories. They had to be true. I had to discover them organically. To search for them, I started with a small memory and began typing as much as I could remember. Sometimes one memory would jog another, and I'd try to link them in a way that felt satisfying. Often I couldn't. I went down a lot of dead ends before finding an emotional through line that felt truthful. That's the challenge with writing organically. It's very inefficient.

As I started digging, I asked myself two questions: What's this story about? And what's it *really* about?

"What's it about" is the plot. It's what happened to me. In the case of "The Marisa Disclaimer," the memory I started with was the woman selling cologne, who told me I wasn't ready for it. It was such a condescending thing to say, and for years, whenever I shared that memory with friends, it was with derision. But then one day I thought, "What if she was right? What if I truly *wasn't* ready for it?" That led me to the very immature way I handled my relationship with Marisa, and it's how "The Marisa Disclaimer" came to be.

When I perform this story to audiences, they always gasp at my confession at the end. They can't believe that this shy and awkward character that they've grown to love could be so cruel. But all of us have done things we're ashamed of. I'm just writing about them. This story is my apology to Marisa. "A Plague upon Your House," "The Ghoul," and "The House on Witherspoon Street" are some of my other stories that are meant to be apologies.

Even when the plot is clear to me, the challenge then becomes how to write about real people in a way that is entertaining but not cruel. In "Escape from Kelly Jelly Belly," even though I changed Kelly's and Leanne's names to protect their identities, I poked fun at them pretty hard. I just couldn't find a way around it. The whole genre of "horrific dating stories" is built around the premise that you are normal, your date is crazy, now let's have a few laughs at their expense. I decided that, to be fair, I would only allow myself to take shots at people as long as I was even harder on myself. My anxieties and insecurities had to be as much in the forefront as theirs. But I couldn't do it in a way that felt self-indulgent or narcissistic.

A personal essay shouldn't feel like a diary entry. It's for the reader's pleasure, not my own. With each passage, I asked myself, "Who is this line for?" If it wasn't for the reader, I'd cut it, because I don't want to alienate anyone. Maybe that fear comes from my background as a television writer. I always picture my audience holding a remote control, quick to find something better to do with their time. Even the seemingly unrelated digressions that I often take in my writing must be related to that theme. In "Rapid Italian," for instance, I take a side trip into the past, where I recount the story of my pet Myrtle the Turtle. But that's only to explain why I sometimes see myself as a turtle—hiding from the world.

To find the structure of these stories, I relied heavily on my background as a screenwriter. In film and television writing, we break every story into three acts. Act Three features the climactic scene that we're building to. It might be the big game, or a trial, or a public event—something where the stakes feel very high. It felt right to borrow this convention for my personal essays. In "The House on Witherspoon Street," Act Three was my appearance on Helen's talk show, which built to the threat of public humiliation. In "Rapid Italian," the climactic scene was my hearing. In "Yellow Belt," it was the judo tournament. Of course, a good story doesn't end at the climax. We have to go past it in order to see the fallout, and this is where we learn from the experience. A story asks the reader to go on a journey, and if the destination doesn't offer a view to something great, then why did the author take them there?

The ending of my early drafts of "Yellow Belt" felt like they didn't do that. Originally, the story concluded in my father's car, with him accepting me for who I was. Even though that ending was true, it felt too easy. I wanted the piece to speak to something larger. Certainly, the violence of that day must've changed that little boy. How could it not? I wanted to know if he could ever go back to who he was before experiencing that kind of violence. I have another strong memory from that time period of building little twig houses beneath the dogwood tree in our front yard. For me, using that memory really helped. It allowed the last scene of the story to be of young Michael trying to rebuild a broken house in order to protect the little creatures—not from the ordinary day-to-day elements, but from an impending storm. He attempts to return to innocence, but can he really go back?

Although it might not be obvious, "*Le Flâneur*" also built to an Act Three moment. It was my outburst at the mansion, but I didn't realize it until much later. When Cynthia and I left that estate sale that day, I was in a really bad mood. As we walked back to the car, she said to me, "You should write a story about this."

"I can't just *write* about stuff," I snapped. "There has to be a story, or else it's just me complaining." Months later, completely by chance, I found the story. I was scrolling through the Internet when I was served an article about the art of *flâneuring*. I had never heard that term before but immediately realized that it would unlock the whole piece. I could write a story about people who judge people.

That brings me to the second question I ask myself when writing a story: What's it *really* about? This question points to the theme. I remember learning about "theme" in my high-school-literature class and wondering if that was just bullshit that teachers invented to sound smart. Now that I'm a writer, I realize that's not the case at all. Theme is simply the one idea that the author explores from various angles. Without a theme, the story would feel disjointed and ultimately unsatisfying.

Generally, I try to focus on one thought. A story might be about living with fear, or isolation, or finding one's identity. "The Ghoul" was about a strange man who lived on my street. But it was *really* about not knowing people—specifically, the people I love. By the end of the piece, I'm no different than Undead Fred, standing in my front yard, incapacitated with grief and unable to let go. I was now the ghoul.

"A Plague upon Your House" is about my life during the beginning of the pandemic. But it's really about fear and anxiety, and how it hurts not just ourselves but the ones we love the most. Without this theme, "Plague" might just as well have been a newspaper article about the pandemic. In fact, that was my initial reservation when I started writing it. I had just completed what I thought was my entire collection when Cynthia said that I needed to write one more story. I thought it was a bizarre thing to say, given that it was my choice to decide how many stories to include. Why did she think one was missing?

At this point, the pandemic had been raging for about a year, and she thought that it was important to write about it, so that, years from now, people might better understand how we lived through it. I didn't think I had anything to add to the conversation. What was I going to document—how we all scrubbed our hands, wore masks, and hid in our homes? It wasn't until that day on the country road, when I sat so peacefully on the double yellow line, that it came to me. Ironically, the pandemic had given me a brief respite from fear. And in that moment, I realized how much I had hurt my beautiful daughters. So even though "A Plague upon Your House" seems to be about the pandemic, it's really about living with anxiety.

The theme of the title story from *A Paper Orchestra* was memories. It started with a magician memorizing everyone's name, then moved toward examining how our own memories work. Interestingly, if I was to pitch the idea of a man meeting up with his ex-girlfriend to a roomful of television writers, two obvious plotlines would emerge: the man and the ex-girlfriend would either have an affair, or one of them would murder the other out of revenge. But the true version, I think, is far more interesting. In real life, I wanted something far more innocent and relatable. I just wanted to know how someone I once loved remembered me. Isn't that what we all want to know—how we're remembered? That's one of the advantages of writing a personal essay. If you're willing to write the truth, it can keep you from writing something cliché.

When I perform, I'm often asked what's it like to write something so incredibly personal, then share it so publicly. Truthfully, the hard part was admitting it on paper. But that's the job of any artist. If you're not willing to be vulnerable in search of the truth, then you should pursue another interest. To me, performing these stories out loud isn't more soul-baring than writing it in the first place. It's only difficult because when I read these memories aloud, I'm reliving them. I'm in the moment, experiencing it with the audience. It's like stepping into a time machine. For stories like "The Ghoul" and "A Plague upon Your House," there's always a moment when it's almost too difficult for me to continue. Like everyone else in the audience, I wish for a different ending that will never come. Putting my memories on paper, then confessing them to an audience, is my chance at redemption. It's also how we connect with each other, because pain is something we all share. Even though the details are mine, I truly believe these stories are all of ours.

Michael

Download a Bonus Story

from Michael Jamin's next collection at
michaeljamin.com/bonus
or scan here:

Dear Reader,

It's my hope that these stories resonated with you in unexpected ways.

If they did... and I know this requires extra work on your part... please tell two friends about *A Paper Orchestra*.

You could also leave a review on Goodreads or wherever you purchased.

Ooh, here's another idea!
Post on social media and tag @michaeljaminwriter.

Thank you so much. I can't wait to share my next book with you.

-Michael

About the Author

As a professional television writer-showrunner, Michael Jamin has made a career of writing what studios pay him to write. But the idea of creating something just for fun ... that hadn't occurred to him in 27 years. *A Paper Orchestra* was conceived to rediscover the joy of writing without expectation. In the process, Michael found something even more important—himself. To see him perform *A Paper Orchestra* as a one-man show, visit: michael jamin.com/upcoming

A Paper Orchestra is also available as an audiobook.

instagram.com/MichaelJaminWriter
facebook.com/MichaelJaminWriter
tiktok.com/@MichaelJaminWriter
goodreads.com/michaeljamin

Made in the USA
Las Vegas, NV
22 May 2024